REPORT OF THE INQUIRY INTO LONDON'S HEALTH SERVICE, MEDICAL EDUCATION AND RESEARCH

Presented to the Secretaries of State for Health and Education by Sir Bernard Tomlinson

October 1992

London: HMSO

First published 1992

ISBN 0 11 321548 7

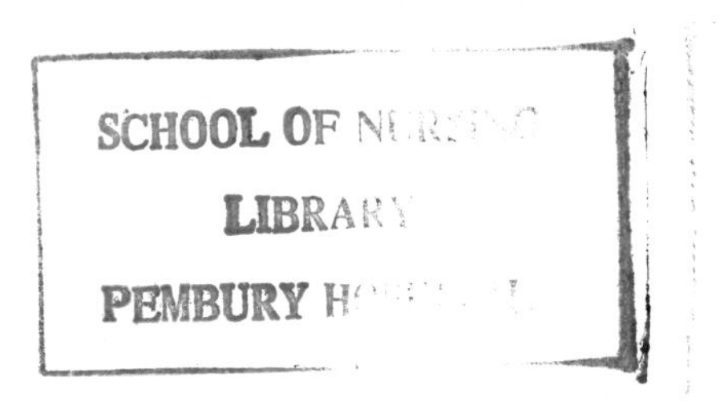

CONTENTS

REPORT

OF THE LONDON INQUIRY

To: The Secretary of State for Health
The Secretary of State for Education

INTRODUCTION

WE WERE asked by your predecessors in October 1991 to advise on the organisation of, and inter-relationships between, the National Health Service and medical education and research in London. Our terms of reference were:

> *To advise the Secretaries of State for Health and Education and Science on how the relevant statutory authorities are addressing the provision of health care in inner London, working within the framework of the reformed NHS, including the balance of primary health services; and the organisation and provision of undergraduate medical teaching, postgraduate medical education and research and development; taking account of:*
>
> - *the health needs of London's resident and day time population;*
> - *the emerging purchasing plans of health authorities and their likely impact on inner London hospitals;*
> - *future developments in the provision of acute and primary care; and*
> - *the need to maintain high quality patient care and, as a foundation for this, high standards of medical teaching research and development.*

2. We were asked to report in about twelve months, so our report is necessarily strategic, rather than detailed. Indeed we were specifically asked not to produce a voluminous report, but instead to provide advice to Ministers and to the Departments as our enquiries progressed, focusing on the management action needed to resolve immediate and foreseeable problems in London. We are well aware that the science and practice of medicine will change radically over the next twenty years, and we have taken account of manifest trends in framing our recommendations. However we have not attempted more speculative or longer-term planning, believing that we have already identified a challenging programme of change for at least the next five years. The mechanism we propose for its implementation will allow for fine-tuning as events unfold.

3. We have taken it as fundamental that the population of London must have as high a standard of general practitioner, hospital, and community-based health care as the rest of the country. Subject to this over-riding requirement, we have aimed to preserve and enhance the national and international role of medical education and research in London and in the many other centres in the UK.

4. In this report we refer to ''inner London'' and ''outer London''. We define these areas as comprising the following district health authorities:

> **Inner London** Bloomsbury and Islington; Camberwell; City and Hackney; Hampstead; Haringey; Lewisham and North Southwark; Newham; Parkside; Riverside; Tower Hamlets; Wandsworth; West Lambeth.
>
> **Outer London** Barking, Havering and Brentwood; Barnet; Bexley; Bromley; Croydon; Ealing; Enfield; Greenwich; Harrow; Hillingdon; Hounslow and Spelthorne; Kingston and Esher; Merton and Sutton; Redbridge; Richmond, Twickenham and Roehampton; Waltham Forest.

5. Our approach has been to meet as many as possible of those involved in the NHS and in medical education and research in London, whether as representatives of users, or as providers, or as purchasers; and to see as many as possible of the institutions concerned. Although we could not meet everyone and see everything, we hope and believe that we have provided the opportunity for all concerned to express their views. We are grateful for the openness and courtesy - and patience - of those we have met; and for the many helpful written submissions we have received. We have, in total, met, visited or spoken to over 1000 individuals, and received 127 written submissions.

6. We have examined the purchasing plans of health authorities both in and outside London, and in making our recommendations, we have borne in mind the changes that will be needed if the objectives of *Care in the Community* and *Health of the Nation* are to be achieved.

7. We have, of course, had the benefit of many previous reports on health care and medical education in London, few of which have been fully implemented. We have also been fortunate in having the extensive published analysis and report by the King's Fund London Commission. While we have kept closely in touch with their work (which started about a year before ours) we have, of course, followed our own approach to the remit we were given. We do not repeat the detailed analyses and statistics about London's health services that are readily available in the King's Fund reports and elsewhere, although we do give data to support our key conclusions. Instead, we draw out what we believe are the inevitable conclusions for the reorganisation of London's services; and point to further work which will be necessary.

8. From the outset we found an acceptance of the need for change, and this has grown as our enquiries progressed. Change is inevitable, owing to the forces of the internal market highlighting inequity and inefficiency in the present distribution of hospital facilities. **If this change is not managed firmly - and in certain cases, urgently - the result will be a serious and haphazard deterioration in health services in London.**

9. We have tried to build upon the ideas already taking shape in London. In particular, we attached great importance to developing a programme for change from the ''bottom up'', building upon consensus, rather than merely devising our own blueprint for action. In this we have been greatly assisted by analyses and proposals from many quarters, but particularly by comprehensive submissions from each of the Thames Regional Health Authorities (RHAs); and from the four of them and London University, acting together. Our Inquiry has galvanised a great deal of continuing study within the RHAs and elsewhere which is still in progress. The results of this work will be important in filling in the detail behind the strategic decisions we recommend in this report.

10. We should also, at this point, place on record our appreciation of the invaluable work of the members of our immediate support unit over the past twelve months, led by Jonathan Stopes-Roe. He, Sue Moylan, Elizabeth Lynam, Martin Markus, Becky Sandhu, David Roberts, Philip Annetts, Bridget MacAlister and Maxine Chambers, have been unstinting in their efforts, and have in turn marshalled the assistance of colleagues in both the Health and Education Departments, for which we are very grateful.

SUMMARY

Primary and community health services

11. Primary and community health services are comparatively underdeveloped in London. Resources need to be diverted from the hospital sector into these services in order to bring standards up to those found elsewhere, and to enable the rationalisation of hospital services in inner London. In particular, additional funds need to be made available for raising the standard of GP premises in inner London. Greater flexibility needs to be introduced into the General Medical Services so that, within designated ''primary care development zones'', FHSAs will be able more effectively to secure strategic health objectives.

12. Greater variety is needed in the methods of delivering primary and community care, and alternative models such as the location of GPs in A & E departments, and the creation of extended local health centres, should be explored. The combination of acute and community services into a single ''whole-district'' provider unit is not helpful, and trusts constituted on this model should be restructured.

The acute sector

13. There is likely to be a significant fall in the requirement for inpatient beds in the inner London hospitals. This will be for two main reasons: withdrawal of patient flows from outside inner London as purchasers secure high quality, but cheaper, services locally; and the continuing trend in the efficiency with which inpatient beds are used, which will enable services to be provided within a smaller estate. By the end of the decade, depending upon the pace and extent of change, these two effects could mean that between 2000 and 7000 beds could become surplus.

14. A number of inner London hospitals are already in financial difficulty as their high overheads, and the mismatch of the scale and nature of their services to current demand, place them at a disadvantage in the reformed NHS. It is essential that work be put in hand now to plan for a more appropriate level of capacity, and to rationalise the many dispersed specialist services. Closures and mergers will be necessary. Proposals in this report, together with changes already planned by the RHAs, will reduce the level of productive acute sector capacity by around 2500 beds.

15. The special health authorities are a further distorting factor in inner London, and should be brought within the NHS internal market as NHS trusts. SIFTR should be reformed to enable all hospitals, including the present SHAs, to compete on a level playing field both for service contracts, and for support for research and teaching overheads. Central provision needs to be made for securing flows of patients with rare conditions which need to be brought

together both for service reasons, and to support research. The services of the SHAs should be subject to the same rationalisation as the other inner London hospitals.

Medical education and research

16. Eight of the nine medical schools in London should merge into four, under the aegis of the four multi-faculty colleges of London University. The ninth, St George's, should for the time being remain on its own. As fewer inpatients come into inner London, and as more treatments are provided in other ways, undergraduate teaching will need to move into primary and community settings, and make greater use of peripheral hospitals. A reduction of around 150 in the intake of medical undergraduates to London is likely to be needed. The nine postgraduate institutions also should in due course be integrated into the four multi-faculty colleges.

Resources

17. It will be essential that adequate transitional funding be provided to ensure that service changes take place in an orderly fashion. The level of such funding will to a large extent dictate the pace of change. Change that is not managed and funded in this way is likely to be chaotic, and will do serious damage to London's health services, and to its medical research and teaching. As savings start to accrue in the acute sector in inner London, they should be used to finance further change, and to shift the balance of expenditure towards community-based health services.

18. Reduction in the capacity of the hospital sector and rationalisation of specialist services will require a corresponding reduction and redeployment in, in particular, consultant numbers. This has not happened when reductions in capacity in the inner London hospitals have taken place previously, but will be necessary if the London hospitals are to survive. Other staff groups will also be affected.

Implementation

19. A high-level Implementation Group should be set up straight away to follow through these recommendations. This Implementation Group should have executive responsibility to secure effective pan-London coordination of a re-structured NHS.

HEALTH NEEDS IN LONDON

20. Although we have not seen it as part of our remit to carry out a comprehensive health needs assessment for the whole of London, we have looked briefly at various indicators. On average, it seems that Londoners are no less healthy than people elsewhere. However it is quite clear to us from the available reports and statistical material, and from the visits and discussions we have had during the course of our Inquiry, that the population of inner London presents a *range* of need unparalleled in the rest of England.

21. Inner London's resident population numbers approximately two and a half million people. These are joined every weekday by about 1.3 million commuters who come to work in the city and, during the course of a year, by around 8 million tourists. London is unique in the British Isles not only because of the volume of its population but also because of its density. Population density is markedly higher in London than in the rest of England and overcrowding is more than twice as prevalent.

22. Population turnover is also high. The four Family Health Services Authorities (FHSAs) with the highest migration rates in England and Wales are all in London. They experienced average annual rates of external migration over the period from 1985 to 1989 in excess of 12%. This does not include migration within the FHSA which may be as high as 20% per year. And, in certain parts of the city, turnover can be as high as between 30% and 40% of the population annually.

23. The challenge of providing health care to the London population is made all the greater by the range and diversity of the individuals that make it up. Extremes of poverty and wealth in London are more marked than elsewhere in England. A higher than average rate of Gross National Product per head is contributed overall by Londoners to the UK economy but, at the same time, it has pockets where the unemployment rate is well above the national average. In terms of the Jarman under-privileged area (UPA) score, all the inner London districts have a score of approximately 20 or more, significantly more in some cases, compared to an England average of zero. The proportion of the population registered with an FHSA which attracts a deprivation allowance to the GP is 54% in inner London compared with an average of approximately 9% for the rest of England.

24. There are high proportions of people from other cultures and for whom English is not their first language. In Tower Hamlets, for example, over 50 languages and dialects are spoken. Many of these people have special needs and experience difficulties in accessing appropriate care and advice. London is also host to high numbers of refugees: latest estimates suggest that there are 120,000 refugees living in the inner city districts of the North Thames Regions alone.

25. There are large numbers of homeless people: in March 1990 there were, on a conservative estimate, 60,000 people in London in temporary accommodation, or sleeping rough. In addition, in some electoral wards it is estimated that 15% or more of the population are not registered with a GP.

26. In the Thames regions as a whole, the overall standardised mortality ratio (SMR) for people under the age of 75 is 92.9 (over the period 1986-1990). In the 12 inner London District Health Authorities (DHAs) it is 112.6. SMRs for people aged between 15 and 64 in inner London stand out even more starkly - they range from 102 to 142, with an overall average of 121.

27. Deaths from AIDS in the Thames regions exceeds those in the rest of the UK put together. The majority of these cases are treated in London. Hospitalisation rates for emergency mental illness are high across the inner London districts, as are the proportions formally detained under the Mental Health Act. In the 15 to 64 age group, the overall SMR for deaths from accidents, poisoning or violence is very high and, where the underlying cause of death is substance abuse, are the highest in the country.

PRIMARY AND COMMUNITY HEALTH SERVICES

28. The long-term trend is an increase in ambulatory and community-based care, and a corresponding fall in the relative importance of hospital inpatient facilities to the provision of health care. Increasingly, chronic conditions such as diabetes, stroke, asthma and HIV/AIDS can be effectively supported in the community, rather than in hospital, and this provides a better service to the patient. In inner London the overwhelming emphasis historically has been on hospital facilities; the potential scale of substitution between secondary and primary care is considerable. This trend requires a shift in the balance of expenditure between the acute, and the primary and community sectors.

29. However in London these latter services are underdeveloped relative to corresponding services in the rest of the country. Although Family Health Services (FHS) expenditure per capita is generally higher in inner city areas than the national average, the level in inner London is less than that in other inner city areas, and the quality of service secured in inner London for this expenditure is poorer. Community nursing services are more expensive in London because staff costs are higher, and the nature of the patient population referred to in the previous chapter makes effective contact more difficult. On average, inner London districts employ around a third fewer district nurses per capita resident population over age 75 than do comparable districts outside London, and the cost per contact in inner London is some 60% greater than the national average, and around twice that in other inner city areas. If the targets in *Health of the Nation* are to be met, and the community care reforms are to be effective, more needs to be spent on these services in London, in four main areas:

> **Human resources** The CHS are labour, rather than capital, intensive: as much as 90% of expenditure is on staff. More and better CHS means more community nurses, and similar staff;
>
> **Community based facilities** GPs' surgeries and health centres, and the services within them, need to be developed into effective focal points for the work of integrated primary health care teams, alongside improved provision of nursing and residential care, and community hospitals.
>
> **Information and management** The "management revolution" in the acute sector has barely touched the CHS yet. Managerial skills and management systems need to be developed to ensure efficient use of resources in a more dispersed service, and better targeting of health need.
>
> **Research** Medical research is predominantly acute hospital based. There is an urgent need for research in primary and community care. Their effectiveness needs to be evaluated, and the quality of care in the

hospital needs to be compared with that in the community setting. The cost-effectiveness of different models of community care, including the so-called hospital outreach services and the extension of consultant services into the community, also need rigorous assessment. More academic departments of primary and community care are needed.

30. As we explain later in this report, a disproportionate amount of London's health resources are spent on hospital services. We ***recommend*** that there should be a gradual and systematic transfer of resources from the acute sector to CHS and FHS budgets in London. Recognising, however, that hospital expenditure is not flexible in the short term, we believe that in the early stages, this re-direction of resources can only be achieved by providing new money in order to facilitate change.

General practice

31. We have visited a number of first class practices, but we are aware that there are also serious inadequacies in primary health services in inner London. The proportions of London GPs on the minor surgery list, or meeting high targets for childhood immunisation and for pre-school boosters, are around a quarter of those found elsewhere. The proportion achieving high targets for cervical cytology is only a tenth of the all-England figure. On average London has far poorer quality general practice premises. 46% of premises in the four inner London FHSAs are below minimum standards, compared with an England average of 7%. London has three times the national percentage of GPs over age 65; twice the proportion of single-handed GPs (although this is not necessarily a sign of poor service); higher incidence of large lists; a lower rate of employment of practice staff compared with other inner cities. These factors mean, for example, poorer access to service, and lower provision of health screening. Significant developments in these services are needed as an early priority.

GP premises

32. The difficulty in securing good quality premises lies at the root of many of the problems surrounding general practice in inner London that have been reported to us. Lack of adequate premises prevents Londoners from receiving the full range of primary health care services. For example, lack of space may prevent practices from taking on partners or support staff and from developing primary health care teams. It can prevent expansion into health promotion, screening, minor surgery, visits of hospital consultants, and other services, which ought to be encouraged in general practice. It can make undergraduate teaching, vocational training and any form of practice research impossible. We note that there is a tendency for GPs to settle in the area in which they undergo postgraduate training; one way to increase the number of GPs in inner London would be to enable more to be trained there by improving postgraduate and continuing education services. Action to tackle

premises problems would help extend the range of primary care services available to London's population, bringing them into line with what is already available in many other parts of the country.

33. Obviously property prices in London are the major obstacle. Many GPs have reported that this factor is inadequately reflected in the financial limits set under the Cost Rent Scheme (CRS). FHSAs have told us that this means they are obliged to approve lower standards of accommodation in high-cost areas. We ***recommend*** that the CRS should be reviewed to ensure that funding is available to raise standards of accommodation in London to the equivalent of those elsewhere, without burdening the GP with more debt than the practice can support. However under the normal CRS rules the GP owns the entire capital value of the property concerned. It would be wrong for some London GPs' holdings to be enhanced at the public expense. We therefore also ***recommend*** that more generous funding should be designed to avoid this inequity.

34. There is very little hard information available on the actual cost of bringing up to standard London GPs' practice premises. We have therefore not attempted a detailed analysis. We have, however, done some preliminary calculations based on figures drawn from illustrative costings by an RHA and FHSA. We assume that, at the very least, funds would be required to bring up to minimum standards those 46% of premises in inner London which currently do not meet them. The purpose of the funds would be either to allow the purchase or conversion of new properties, or to meet the costs of major improvements to new rented or existing properties. At an average cost per practice of £500,000 the total cost would be of the order of £130 million. If, in addition, four new units on the lines of the West Lambeth Community Care Centre were developed, at a cost of £2 million each, we envisage a possible total cost of around £140 million over several years.

35. GPs have also reported difficulties and long delays with local planning authorities in attempting to set up or develop practice premises. Some FHSAs provide support to GPs on premises related matters. We ***recommend*** that there should be generally available to GPs on a pan-London basis expert assistance or "premises facilitators" to help in the planning, design and acquisition of premises, liaising with local authority planning departments, and setting up financial arrangements including the complexities of the CRS.

36. GPs have also complained that DHAs make poor landlords of health centres, where maintenance has frequently been seriously neglected, and the GPs have little or no control over, or flexibility in, their use and development of the building. We ***recommend*** that, where it is not possible for the GPs to own or lease the property themselves, it should be entrusted to a management committee including representatives of the GPs and other professional users. We understand that the Department recently commissioned a study of the arrangements for financing GP accommodation in health centres. We believe

the current arrangements are not working effectively, and trust that the study will lead to improvements.

37. We have been told that DHAs and trusts are sometimes reluctant to cooperate by selling surplus hospital estate for conversion into facilities suitable for the development of primary care. We ***recommend*** that FHSAs should take a more pro-active role in the provision and leasing of premises to GPs so as to meet FHSAs' strategic health care objectives. The major reorganisation of capital resources in London which we recommend in this report will provide more opportunities for cost-effective re-use of assets. Clearly holders of public assets are obliged to maximise their disposal value, but where a windfall gain accrues to part of the NHS, there should be a means of ensuring that the benefit is applied to the highest priority in the NHS as a whole. We make recommendations bearing upon this point in paragraph 227.

Increasing flexibility in the General Medical Services

38. FHSAs are increasingly closely involved with their corresponding DHAs in health needs assessment and service commissioning. However some have reported that it is more difficult for them to define and commission the services they seek from family doctors in the General Medical Services (GMS) than it is for their counterparts in the DHAs who commission hospital and community health services (HCHS). This is because, unlike the NHS contracts for HCHS which are created by a DHA, the terms of an FHSA's contracts with its "providers" are almost entirely centrally determined through negotiation between the profession and the Department of Health, on behalf of the Secretary of State.

39. Many of the problems we have identified stem from this. In particular, we see little direct local management accountability for services delivered and for resources consumed in the general medical services. Although the 1990 GP contract sought to generate improvements in the quality and range of services through financial incentives, through a stronger role for FHSA management, and through promoting consumer choice, these influences are not making the necessary impact in London. The scope for FHSAs to identify health needs and to target resources and activity at them remains limited; for example, an FHSA may pay a deprivation allowance but it has little feedback on, or control over, the resulting service.

40. We have identified a number of options for tackling these problems. At the most radical end of the spectrum would be a shift to local contracts between FHSAs and practices, in place of the present centrally negotiated contract. This would put FHSAs in a position to define specific services in contracts, to meet local needs, and to hold GPs to account for their delivery. We believe this approach worth exploring further, although we recognise that it represents a wholesale departure from current arrangements, with major legal and financial implications, and would offer neither easy nor early solutions to London's problems.

41. We therefore ***recommend*** that the Department, the profession, and NHS management should also look critically at the way in which the operation of the current financial incentives and management powers are falling short in London, and should explore the scope for improvement. We have noted, for example, that FHSAs vary considerably in their degree of development beyond the old Family Practitioner Committee (FPC) role. Not all seem to be aware of their existing powers, and not all use them effectively. Some of these questions may need solutions that extend beyond London. But as far as London is concerned, we ***recommend*** that the Department of Health should explore with GPs' representatives the scope for designating parts of London as "primary care development zones" in which some of the normal arrangements could be suspended, or otherwise modified, so as to secure a better service, in line with local health needs.

42. Similarly, FHSAs have no management control over the allocation within their areas of the most important resource: skilled manpower, in the form of GPs. At the overall level, this is the responsibility of the (centrally-based) Medical Practices Committee (MPC). We have discussed this with the MPC, and we recognise the valuable work it does, within the terms of its remit. We recognise a continuing need for a national overview of the distribution of GP manpower. But we do question whether the same degree of MPC involvement is needed in the local configuration of manpower and partnerships. We therefore ***recommend*** that, within the London "primary care development zones", the MPC should devolve to FHSAs the responsibility for deciding, in consultation with the profession locally, how the GP manpower available to the area might best be organised to meet local needs. This would facilitate coordinated plans for GP manpower, premises and practice staff.

43. Likewise at the individual level, practices need to be able to develop a mix of qualities, skills and services appropriate to the needs of the area. Management and profession need to work together on this. We therefore ***recommend*** that FHSAs ensure that local needs are given their proper weight in the process of partnership development. We also ***recommend*** that FHSAs should have the power, when appointing a new GP principal, to reject all applicants and re-advertise, if none of the applicants meets the objective requirements set by the FHSA.

Practice nurses

44. The number of practice nurses has increased rapidly since the introduction of the GP contract. Their training needs are being assessed, and there are some good developments in joint training with health authority community nurses. But we have been told that practice nurses are not always being released for regular training. FHSAs are able, when agreeing direct reimbursement for practice staff costs, to make such agreements conditional on appropriate training being arranged, and to take account of training costs

in the reimbursement arrangements. Training should be developed in conjunction with nursing audit, and this too should be addressed by the FHSAs. We were pleased to learn that the Task Group on Primary Care Nursing which is due to report in November is to offer guidance on the action FHSAs can take to promote good employment practice. We commend this to the attention of London's FHSAs.

Extending the availability of primary care

45. For a number of groups - the homeless, drug abusers, some members of minority ethnic groups, commuters, visitors - GP services are for various reasons not easily accessible. For some groups they may not be acceptable either, and even if they were, it is likely that many street homeless, for example, would be unacceptable to other users of GP services. Voluntary organisations can meet this need for many groups, and purchasing authorities should ensure that they are adequately resourced so that a comprehensive range of services is available to these groups. Even for registered patients, GP services may not be easily available outside normal hours. The result is what is often termed ''inappropriate attendance'' at accident and emergency (A & E) departments by patients who could more appropriately have been dealt with by a member of a general practice team - if such were available to them.

46. London has significantly higher usage of A & E: new attendances at A & E in inner London hospitals average 405 per 1000 population, compared to the England average of 234 per 1000. The London Ambulance Service has told us that there is a tendency in London for some GPs to tell their patients to dial 999 if the condition worsens. This does not represent adequate primary care.

47. The care of the most vulnerable groups must be catered for in DHA and FHSA purchasing plans. From the patient's point of view, A & E attendance may be entirely appropriate. We ***recommend*** that three responses to this situation be pursued in parallel:

- improve the scope and accessibility of general practice along the lines we have set out above;

- where there is a high proportion of primary care attenders, adapt hospital A & E services in a cost-effective way, for example by including GPs and nurse practitioners amongst the A & E staff so that patients get the service which is appropriate to their requirements. This approach has been successfully piloted at King's College Hospital and has now been extended to Lewisham Hospital. It offers advantages to patients by providing better advice than is often given by less experienced doctors, to the hospital in reducing inappropriate investigations, treatments and admissions, and to junior doctors in better training;

- explore alternative models of primary care, in collaboration with voluntary organisations and others, including the appointment of salaried or sessionally paid GPs to work alongside traditional partnerships; and the creation of extended primary care centres at strategic locations in inner city areas.

COMMUNITY HEALTH SERVICES

48. Community health services should complement general practice in providing integrated support to the health of the general population. They should also support the more economic and effective use of hospital and residential care. In cases where community care is no cheaper than hospital care, it should allow improved quality of service. The main requirement is for community nursing and paramedical services, but these, and more specialised schemes such as ''Hospital at Home'', and paediatric home nursing have been slow to develop in London.

49. As with family health services, we believe that there has to be a systematic transfer of resources, over a period of years, from hospital to CHS expenditure in London. Typically, a one per cent reduction in a DHA's hospital service expenditure is equivalent to around a seven per cent increase in its CHS budget. Development of community-based schemes would need pump priming to enable resources to be released from hospital care. Again, since expenditure is not very flexible in the short term, we ***recommend*** that there should be a transitional increase in funding specifically aimed at building up the CHS in advance of a reduction in acute sector capacity. Moreover, while the acute sector is under the financial strain of change, its tendency to draw resources out of the CHS must be countered. To be fully effective, the transfer of funds needs to be supported by additional measures, given the history and relative strengths of the parties concerned. We outline these below.

Whole-district trusts

50. The ''poor relation'' status of the community health services to the acute sector is, historically, nowhere more apparent than in the context of the inner London teaching districts. To their credit, some purchasers and providers have been seeking to rectify this, and to establish a ''seamless service'' between hospital and community-based health services. One way of achieving this is said to be by combining acute and community services under single management in a trust.

51. However the creation of ''whole-district'' trusts goes against the grain of two of the key concepts of the NHS reforms: the purchaser-provider split;

and the NHS trust model of provider organisation. The re-designation of the services of an entire DHA as falling within a new NHS trust does little to focus the attention of each provider on the delivery of a specific service; nor does it enable purchasers to re-examine their priorities and place contracts in new ways.

52. We agree with the Audit Commission's view, in its report *Homeward Bound* that if CHS are broken up and spread among clinical directorates this will reduce their flexibility. When both services are placed under the same management, the prestigious inner London teaching hospitals tend to draw resources away from the CHS. Many purchasers, and the contracts they place, are insufficiently robust to prevent such misallocation of resources. This may not be equally so throughout the country, and indeed may have less strength in some of the outer London districts; in any case, this balance should eventually change. As a general principle, however, we ***recommend*** that in future the formation of whole-district trusts should be discouraged unless there is a clear case that service benefits will be gained.

53. We do not believe that this case has been made for the four existing and prospective whole-district trusts involving London teaching hospitals (Royal London, St George's, St Bartholomew's and King's). Accordingly, we ***recommend*** that all four should be unpicked in this respect, and separate management arrangements made for the CHS in the districts affected. We note that, in the case of King's, there are two nearby CHS trusts (Optimum and West Lambeth) which could readily manage services to the Camberwell area.

54. We recognise that unpicking the Royal London trust, being already firmly in existence, would need careful planning. However the problems that have been reported to us as arising in Tower Hamlets CHS seem to be a good example of the disadvantages of whole-district trusts. We therefore ***recommend*** that these acute and community services should be separated.

Primary health care teams

55. Many more practices now employ practice nurses, but the development of Primary Health Care Teams (PHCTs), which include district nurses and health visitors among others, has been slow in London for understandable reasons. The higher proportion of single handed practices and poor premises has hindered the adoption of this approach, and until recently there have been CHS managers, and there still are some GPs, who show little interest in these developments.

56. Many of the nursing team members of PHCTs are also members of the multidisciplinary neighbourhood nursing teams which have been developed in over half the health authorities in inner London. Early evidence shows that economies of scale and improvements in access can be gained by having a

single local manager coordinating resources, and reviewing the skill and grade mix necessary for the services to a local population ranging, in London, from 20-40,000.

57. These neighbourhood nursing teams can also cater for those who do not have GPs (which can be at least 15% of the population in some wards in central London). They are often the only contact with the health service for homeless people, drug users and those with mental health problems. In some health authorities, only half the referrals to these district nursing services are from general practice.

58. Because of the density of the population in central London and the importance of assessing local needs within local authority social work areas, the services of both GPs and CHS staff should be aggregated within localities considerably smaller than the overall purchasing authority. Services organised on such a locality basis, supporting a number of general practices (including PHCTs), would improve the position of single-handed GPs, would improve links with social services, and would provide a base for multi-disciplinary undergraduate and postgraduate education and training. We ***recommend*** that this mode of organisation be adopted by community trusts and FHSAs.

Nursing home and non-acute provision

59. In terms of available places per head of resident population of age 65 and over, inner London has less than a third of the level of nursing home provision in England as a whole. This lack of provision inevitably adds to the blocking of acute beds in hospitals. The main reason for this is of course the cost of suitable property. Most nursing and residential home provision is made by the private sector, but the higher costs would affect the NHS equally. We do not propose that the NHS should attempt to make good this deficit entirely; however there is action that the NHS could take.

60. We have been impressed by several initiatives to provide low-dependency accommodation annexed to the main hospital, as a more cost-effective and better quality service to patients who cannot be discharged directly to their own homes. We ***recommend*** that more of such provision should be made. We have also been impressed by the concept of the "community hospital" which has been implemented in West Lambeth, and which provides on a planned basis access to low-intensity care for the patients of a group of GPs. We ***recommend*** that this model should also be more widely adopted.

MENTAL ILLNESS AND MENTAL HANDICAP

61. The policy of closing large mental hospitals for the mentally ill and those with learning difficulties in favour of caring for them in the community has been pursued in London as elsewhere in the country for several years.

However, unlike other cities, the proportion of people with psychiatric problems is greater because of the flow into London of vulnerable people with mental illness, drug addiction problems, alcoholism and multiple social problems. They form a significant proportion of the street homeless and of occupants of hostels and other temporary accommodation. Such individuals have the same right as others to good medical care and social support, but the provision of accommodation for the former residents of large mental illness hospitals has not met demand, and community-based care has been undermined in many parts of London by a lack of trained professionals including psychologists, occupational therapists, community psychiatric nurses and social workers.

62. The homeless and socially deprived in particular require easy access to the services they need, but we have been told that the number of drop-in centres and similar facilities has been falling. Although there are well-developed community mental health services in some districts, they are relatively few in number in London as a whole. As a consequence, the problems posed by the mentally ill and disabled increases pressures on families (where they exist), on GP services, acute psychiatric admission units (especially those close to major rail and bus terminals), local authorities and voluntary organisations. We ***recommend*** that urgent efforts should be made to develop fully resourced community mental health teams in those inner London districts that lack them.

63. It has been reported to us that existing acute psychiatric admission beds in London are too few to cope with the number of referrals from the community. In some units as many as 80% of the acutely mental ill are statutorily detained, and this proportion is far in excess of the average for England. Given the pressure from former residents of mental illness hospitals both in London and outside, and the fact that 50% of those in temporary accommodation or sleeping rough (in the region of 60,000 at any one time) have significant psychiatric problems, we ***recommend*** that there should be a review of the provision of acute psychiatric admission beds.

64. In addition to dealing with exclusively psychiatric patients, general hospital psychiatric units provide services in liaison with other specialties. A quarter of acute medical admissions have evidence of mental illness, 30% of acute medical and surgical admissions have alcohol problems, and as many as half the patients in all medical specialties referred for investigation do not have physical disorders to account for their symptoms. However we are aware that such services are sometimes neglected, or transferred to specifically psychiatric units, which, as we have noted above, are not always adequately provided or well sited. We ***recommend*** that facilities for ''liaison psychiatry'' should be included in the review of specialties to which we refer in paragraph 150.

65. Because major psychiatric illness is often chronic, with acute episodes, care for those who suffer from it should include the facility to move easily to

and from the community into acute units. Therefore, in distinction to our recommendations in paragraph 52 on whole-district trusts in general, we ***recommend*** the establishment of mental health trusts with responsibility for both acute and community services as the most appropriate managerial arrangement.

66. Facilities for caring for the elderly mentally ill and frail are insufficient for the demands placed upon them, and the cost of caring for such people in the private sector is higher in London than elsewhere. It has been reported to us that as a result, beds for both the acutely physically ill and for those with acute mental disorders are often blocked and this is clearly an inefficient use of acute bed capacity. We ***recommend*** that, when planning community resources for the mentally ill and frail, emphasis should be given to the provision of nursing homes and day centres close to patients' homes.

Commissioning and providing services in the community

67. Rather than linking acute and CHS services in combined trusts, we believe that the first priority is to develop a more constructive link between the primary and the community health services. We note that there is increasing cooperation between DHAs and FHSAs in the development of integrated commissioning strategies. In some areas this is leading to a more or less formal delegation from the DHA to the FHSA of budgets and responsibilities for commissioning CHS, alongside the primary health care services for which they are already responsible. We welcome this move towards more coherent purchasing of the range of services which are delivered to patients broadly in a community setting by a PHCT.

68. We believe that as between DHAs and FHSAs, the greater expertise in this field rests for the most part with FHSAs. We therefore ***recommend*** that for the immediate future, responsibility and resources for commissioning the full range of PHCT services should be fully delegated to the commissioning element of the FHSA. However this will require strengthening of the management capacity of the FHSAs, to which we refer in paragraph 168. Looking a little further to the future, we recognise that the development of GP fundholding and other arrangements for GPs to influence HCHS purchasing, will call for a capacity to look at the totality of population needs and to commission services accordingly. Our recommendation will need to be revisited at that stage. We believe, however, that action to strengthen the commissioning of primary health care (in its widest sense) is the essential next step.

69. Several community-based health workers, for example nurse facilitators, ethnic minority workers, HIV workers, are employed by DHAs and FHSAs with overlapping responsibilities. We ***recommend*** that purchasers

should ensure that such functions are integrated, and that the staff, whichever organisation they belong to, work together cost-effectively.

LINKS WITH SOCIAL SERVICES

70. Many local authority services are essential components of health and social care. These include: the provision of help in the home for the disabled, the elderly and the infirm; housing; and the support role of social workers (working within hospitals and in the community). It is clear that the planning and provision of patient services in the community requires close liaison between local authorities and the health purchasers. The implementation of Care in the Community in April 1993, when local authorities assume new areas of responsibility, will make this liaison even more important. Sufficient priority must be given to the development of joint care plans to meet the needs of the local population and individual patients. We have not been able to study this area closely, but we note that both health authorities and local authority social services departments are new to their respective roles as purchasers of care, and will need to ensure that the necessary new skills and working relationships are developed quickly, and that complementary services are secured.

71. With this in mind, we particularly ***recommend*** that health purchaser (FHSA and DHA) and local authority boundaries should be coterminous (see paragraph 170). A health purchasing authority with more than one local authority within its boundary should ensure that suitable, locality-based, strategies are developed in consultation with the appropriate social service departments. We also ***recommend*** that clear points of contact are maintained between primary and community health services and local social workers, preferably by means of the association of social workers and care managers with primary health care teams.

72. It has been put to us that the heavy flows of patients around London, and the steady rationalisation of services into fewer hospitals (which we recommend needs to be taken further) causes unfair distortions in social service expenditure for the local authorities which happen to host major hospitals. They are required to provide social workers in the hospitals, but cannot share the cost with the local authorities where patients live. We therefore ***recommend*** that these statutory arrangements be re-examined to find a way of more nearly reflecting the purchaser-provider split which applies in the NHS.

THE ACUTE SECTOR

73. Inner London is dominated by the teaching hospitals and medical schools. These high cost hospitals provide a different mix of services to that found in the rest of England: there is a concentration of specialised services; a higher proportion of all admissions is for elective treatments, and through A & E; and a lower proportion is on emergency GP referral. Inner London hospitals are significant providers of inpatient care (particularly elective surgery and highly specialised services) to patients from outer London and the rest of the Thames regions. The special health authorities (SHAs) are another unique feature of the London hospital scene adding around 1800 beds to inner London. With their associated postgraduate research institutes they together form an important component of London's and the nation's research and teaching base, and a major part of the Thames regions' specialist services.

74. Many GPs have told us that they have difficulty in securing emergency admissions to inner London hospitals. However the Emergency Bed Service (EBS) caseload (which could be taken as one measure of pressure on emergency admissions) has fallen slightly over the last eighteen months, and the EBS referee rate, which indicates the proportion of cases in which the EBS requires a hospital to take a patient, has remained steady during that time. The explanation of this apparent discrepancy may partly lie in greater referral by GPs, and self-referral by patients themselves, to A & E as a means of securing emergency admission, thus contributing to the higher rate of admission through A & E overall.

75. Waiting times for elective treatment in the inner London teaching hospitals are on average longer than elsewhere, but have improved considerably over the last year, as Table 1 shows:

TABLE 1

COMPARATIVE WAITING TIMES

Hospitals in:	Percentage of patients waiting:			
	Over 1 year		Over 2 years	
	June 91	June 92	June 91	June 92
Inner London (teaching)	28.6	14.7	11.7	0.7
Thames Regions	21.7	11.4	7.2	0.2
England	17.8	9.0	5.3	0.1

76. These problems with both emergency and elective admissions are attributable to a combination of factors: inadequate primary and community care, the organisation of the acute sector in London, and the nature of patient

flows. In 1992/93 spending per inner London resident on hospital services, *after* weighting for morbidity and mortality (which adds about 5%), and *allowing* for excess London costs, will be 20% greater than the average for England. The problems of the inner London hospitals are plainly not due to any overall lack of resources.

77. In this section we examine how patient flows to inner London hospitals are likely to change, and how services could be organised more efficiently to care for the London population and other patients who need to come to London for treatment. Changes in patient flows and hospital organisation have been taking place for some years, and have already reduced the number of hospital beds in inner London by 5000 over the last ten years. Furthermore, the developments in primary and community health services which we have recommended could reduce the pressure on acute hospital facilities in three ways: first, by promoting a healthier population not needing such frequent hospital admission; secondly by providing health care in more appropriate settings in the community; and thirdly by enabling "blocked" beds to be released more rapidly.

78. The separation of the purchaser and provider roles is the biggest change in the NHS since its inception. It will bring about significant changes in many parts of the country, particularly in large conurbations, but most extensively in and around London. It, and the introduction of capitation funding, has highlighted the vulnerability of London's major hospitals, which were already facing reductions in their relatively well-funded positions as a result of the move towards Resource Allocation Working Party targets. Already it is clear that a number of teaching hospitals will not be viable in their present form when purchasers plan services on the basis of their assessment of the needs of their resident populations.

Estimating the demand for inpatient beds in London

79. Non-London districts and GPs are increasingly keen to secure all but the most highly specialised services locally (and at lower cost). We have formed the impression that the inner London hospitals take little account of just how far services have developed outside London, and of the extent to which capacity and expertise could rapidly be brought into play.

80. We have looked at a number of theoretical factors affecting the supply of, and demand for, acute sector resources in inner London. We conclude that the net effect will be that substantially fewer traditional hospital inpatient beds will be needed in the future. Our analysis is based on broad assumptions, to give an indication of the scale of change that will be needed over the next five to ten years. It is in four parts:

- changes in patient flows into inner London hospitals, other than the SHAs, from outside inner London

- changes in usage of inner London non-SHA hospitals by their local residents

- changes in patient flows to SHA hospitals

- effects of increased efficiency in all hospitals.

81. Table 2 summarises the effects of various assumptions about patient flows, at different levels of efficiency (which we define in paragraph 90). The table starts (Section 1) with baseline activity as in 1990/91, and shows how, without any changes in patient flows, that level of activity, if conducted at higher levels of efficiency, would release surplus beds.

TABLE 2

ACUTE BEDS RELEASED IN INNER LONDON HOSPITALS
BY CHANGED PATIENT FLOWS AT VARIOUS LEVELS OF EFFICIENCY

Patient flows	**Acute beds released**			
	Level of efficiency (beds per 1000 episodes):			
	Current (see note)	14	12.8	10
Current flows unchanged (year 1990/91)				
1. Non-SHA hospitals [total 9457 beds]	0	2740	3310	4660
SHA hospitals [total 1845 beds]	0	625	730	980
Changed flows				
2. Non-inner London patients withdraw from inner London non-SHAs:				
A. All elective cases	1960	1390	1270	990
B. "Local acute" elective cases only	790	560	510	400
3. Inner London residents' use of inner London non-SHAs changes:				
A. In proportion to capitation change	500	360	330	260
B. Half the effect of A above	250	180	165	130
4. SHA funding redistributed nationally in capitation; flows to SHAs reflect all Thames's share, plus:				
A. Half of non-Thames's share	650	430	400	310
B. Three-quarters of non-Thames's share	325	215	200	155
Total beds released				
5. Total of sections 1+2+3+4 above:				
Maximum (scenarios A)	3110	5545	6040	7200
Minimum (scenarios B)	1365	4320	4915	6325

Note: Bed use in 1990/91 was 19.7 per 1000 episodes in non-SHA hospitals, and 21.2 per 1000 in SHA hospitals.

Changes in patient flows into inner London

82. The change to resident-based funding in 1991/92 placed in the hands of outer- and non-London DHAs and GP fundholders the funds with which they now purchase referrals to inner London hospitals for residents of their districts. This, and the subsequent moves towards weighted capitation will have a major effect on the flow of patients into inner London hospitals. Our examination of the contracting intentions of these non-inner London purchasers shows clearly that they will increasingly choose not to use the inner London hospitals, especially for routine elective surgery.

83. Of all acute cases treated in inner London non-SHAs, 21% are elective cases coming from outer London or other Thames districts, and a further 2% come from the rest of England. Of all these elective cases, about half are for routine "local acute" services (ie: general surgery, general medicine, urology, paediatrics, trauma and orthopaedics, thoracic medicine, dermatology, genito-urinary medicine and gynaecology). Clearly, the effect on demand for acute sector capacity in inner London depends upon how much of these flows are withdrawn, and at what speed. If, in an extreme case, all elective acute services to patients from outside inner London were withdrawn, there would be a need for around 1960 fewer beds in inner London hospitals. However if only "local acute" elective services were withdrawn, 790 fewer beds would be needed. This scenario is set out in Section 2 of Table 2.

Changes in hospital use by inner London residents

84. Weighted capitation is intended to ensure the equitable distribution of revenue throughout the country, so that inner London districts will have the same purchasing power per resident as elsewhere. Allowance is made for the higher costs arising in London, and for deprivation factors; we comment further on these points in paragraph 233. Under current formulae, all inner London districts except Tower Hamlets and City and Hackney will lose under full weighted capitation.

85. It is not possible to predict how inner London DHAs will respond to changes in their capitation. Gainers may buy more acute services, or they may spend the extra funds on other services. Likewise losers may reduce the level of activity in one or another sector, or they may require the hospitals to provide a "cheaper" mix of services using the same level of capacity. If the acute sector activity currently purchased by inner London districts from inner London hospitals changed (up or down) in proportion to each district's current distance from its full weighted capitation, around 500 fewer beds would be needed in the hospitals. This scenario is set out in Section 3 of Table 2.

86. We have looked at the possible effects of demographic change in inner London, and of trends in the use of hospital services generally, on the level of use inner London residents may be expected to make of local hospitals over the next five years. We would expect the two effects to be relatively small,

and to work in opposite directions. We do not consider that they would make a significant impact on the general order of bed surpluses which will build up over that time. This conclusion will need to be reviewed in the light of 1991 Census data, when they become available.

Changes in patient flows to SHA hospitals

87. In paragraph 161 we recommend that the SHAs should be brought into the internal market, but with additional funding through a modified service increment for teaching and research (SIFTR) to cover the excess service costs attributable to their academic commitments. Hitherto, the SHAs' services have been a free good to purchasers, worth overall around £230 million (excluding a notional element which meets research overhead costs), of which some £75 million directly benefits inner London districts. This causes a significant distortion in equitable weighted capitation. Once the SHAs are funded through internal market contracts, they would cease to be centrally funded, and the £230 million would be distributed nationally through the capitation system.

88. This would mean that the Thames regions would receive 29% of the money, whereas they currently use 87% of SHA services. The inner London districts would receive only 6% of the funds, whereas they currently use 33% of the services. The Thames regions may well spend most of their share of the "SHA money" in the SHAs, since the specialist services of the SHAs are reasonably convenient to their residents (and we assume that our recommendations in the section on SHA funding (page 42) will enable their services to be competitively priced). However non-Thames purchasers may spend much of their share with other specialist providers. If all the Thames share of the reallocated money flows back to the SHAs, but only half of the non-Thames share of the allocation does so, there would be a reduction in demand for beds in the SHAs of some 650. If three-quarters of the non-Thames allocation flowed back, the loss of demand would be equivalent to 325 beds. This scenario is set out in Section 4 of Table 2.

Changes in efficiency of inner London hospitals

89. In addition to the effects of the internal market and weighted capitation, there is throughout the NHS a steady trend towards greater efficiency in using hospital resources: length of stay and turnover interval are shortening; and there is greater use of day surgery. Inner London hospitals are significantly less efficient in these respects than those elsewhere, even after allowing for the effects of their case-mix and teaching commitments. It is likely that the purchasers of services provided in inner London will demand efficiency levels similar to those found in the rest of the country, and indeed the survival of many hospitals will depend upon it.

90. A simple measure of efficiency is the number of beds used per 1000 episodes of acute care. In 1990/91 inner London DHAs on average used 19.7

beds per 1000 episodes: within this average the teaching hospitals used 20.3, and non-teaching hospitals used 16.5; the SHAs used 21.2. By comparison, teaching districts outside London, as a group, used 18.8 beds per 1000 episodes. And in 1989/90 the most efficient 10% of districts nationally used 14 beds per 1000 episodes. Although efficiency cannot be increased overnight, hospitals everywhere, including those in London, have shown a steady trend of improvement. In fact, the current trend in efficiency in inner London districts suggests that over the next five years - by 1998 - they would be using on average 12.8 beds per 1000 acute episodes. However by then, the national trend would have taken the national average level to 10 beds per 1000 episodes.

91. If all inner London hospitals achieved the 14 beds per 1000 episodes level of efficiency, then on the basis of their 1990/91 activity and bed numbers, 2740 fewer beds would have been needed. At the efficiency level of 12.8 beds per 1000 episodes, 3310 fewer beds would be needed. The Thames RHAs are confident that an average level of 14 beds per 1000 overall can readily be achieved, and that 12.8 is attainable. If inner London matched the likely national level of efficiency in five year's time of 10 beds per 1000 episodes, the theoretical saving due to increased efficiency would be 4660 beds. Likewise, if the SHAs achieved bed usage rates of 14, 12.8 or 10 beds per 1000 acute episodes, the theoretical saving in beds on their 1990/91 baseline activity would be 625, 730 or 980 respectively.

92. Clearly, if beds had already been saved as a result of the withdrawal of inflows from outside inner London, fewer beds would be available to be saved by efficiency improvements. The effect of working at higher levels of efficiency, both on the baseline activity, and on the various scenarios for changes in patient flows, is shown by the columns in Table 2.

93. The teaching hospitals and SHAs may not achieve the highest levels of throughput for all their services, where their academic commitment places extra burdens on the service. The cost of this in the teaching hospitals is currently paid for by SIFTR, and in paragraph 163 we recommend that a reformed SIFTR should apply to all eligible hospitals, including SHAs. However we recognise that the extra beds still have to be planned for.

Summary of effects on bed capacity

94. Overall, inner London hospitals face a significant reduction in demand for inpatient beds due to the effects of the internal market and weighted capitation. Quite apart from this, developments in service and efficiency will also mean a reduced need for beds. In our analysis the effects on bed numbers of likely increases in efficiency considerably outweigh the effects of changes in patient flows. In any case, this all means that the total requirement for inpatient capacity in the inner London acute hospitals will shrink substantially over the next five years.

95. Section 5 of Table 2 shows the range of effects, given different assumptions about changes in patient flows and efficiency. Assuming no change in efficiency whatever, at least 1365 of the 11302 beds in inner London hospitals (including SHAs) in 1990/91 would become surplus, once the internal market settles down. On modest assumptions about increases in efficiency, that surplus might range from 4320 to 5545, depending upon how patient flows changed. If the effects on patient flows were more marked, and efficiency gains greater, the maximum surplus we have estimated could be considerably larger. We cannot forecast the total effect, nor the pace, of change. However there are certain minimum short- and medium-term measures which can be identified and put in hand straight away.

Managing a reduction in acute sector capacity

96. Our analysis of the future need for acute beds in inner London demonstrates that the capacity of the inner London hospitals must, over time, be brought into balance with the demands that will henceforth be made upon them. A reduction in capacity on the scale needed cannot be achieved by piecemeal bed closures and efficiency savings in each hospital. Merely slimming down every hospital in London leaves in place fixed costs, overheads and under-used buildings. We ***recommend*** that whole hospital sites should be taken out of service altogether, and the essential services within them relocated; the capital stock involved should be sold or turned to alternative use; and the staff concerned should be redeployed.

97. A managed run-down of the most vulnerable hospitals is therefore essential to remove surplus capacity in an orderly way. The continuity of patient care must be assured while the services are rationalised to the level and disposition needed in future in inner London. If hospital capacity is closed faster than demand falls, waiting times in inner London hospitals will rise. If it is not closed fast enough, some - perhaps many - hospitals will fall into a spiral of financial decline as their fixed costs have to be spread over a smaller patient base, leading to higher unit prices, and in turn to further reduction in patient volume. In both cases Londoners will be the main losers. We estimate that, if no action is taken to reduce capacity, and if only the "local acute" services referred to in paragraph 83 were withdrawn over two years, the resulting price inflation (over and above all other inflation) in inner London hospitals would be around 10% per year.

98. Closure of a teaching hospital is a complex management task: the needs of patients have to be met elsewhere; many specialist services and research units must be relocated; staff take time to redeploy; referral patterns and professional relationships take time to change; educational changes must be carefully planned; buildings take time to adapt or sell. However we ***recommend*** that decisions on the first hospitals to close should be made urgently, so as to remove uncertainty and to enable planning to start.

99. Bridging capital, redundancy compensation and other costs will need to be met in advance of the eventual savings which would arise from a more efficient and effective disposition of resources. These costs of re-organisation must not be borne solely by inner London providers' prices. We ***recommend*** that these factors should be recognised by the provision of adequate transitional funding. The pace of change cannot proceed faster than transitional funding permits.

100. This funding could flow in either of two ways: first, to the purchasers of services from the London hospitals, to allow them to meet the excess running costs their providers will face during the process of adaptation. Secondly, funds could flow direct to the hospitals themselves in order to meet specific one-off costs of change. In either case, such subventions should be directed to specific hospitals, for a specific time, on condition that they adopt a clear management plan for matching their capacity to current and foreseeable demand.

Assessment of inner London hospitals

101. We have carried out a preliminary assessment of the viability and strategic service position of each of the main inner London hospitals. In doing this, we have considered:

- the vulnerability of the hospital in terms of:
    - the effects of the internal market on patient inflows
    - changes in hospital use by local residents
    - excess costs
    - the size of the resident population served
- current financial pressures
- the condition of, and alternative uses for, buildings.

Vulnerability of individual hospitals

102. In line with our analysis of likely changes in patient flows, a hospital which draws patients more heavily from outside its home district, or from immediately neighbouring districts, risks facing reduced demand for its services as distant purchasers seek to secure services more locally. Statistics on the district of origin of patients treated in hospitals are available only on the basis of district of treatment. Where that district has more than one hospital, it is not possible to identify uniquely the individual hospital of treatment. Nevertheless, there are significant variations in the proportion of

the acute caseload of the main inner London provider units which comes from non-neighbouring districts. These percentages are set out in column A of Table 3.

103. Where the residents of a district show a heavier use of acute hospital services (wherever they are provided) than would be expected from national utilisation rates, after standardising for age, Jarman UPA score (as a proxy for morbidity) and mortality, it is likely that the district will be unable to maintain that level under its true weighted capitation. A hospital facing a local purchaser which is in this position may therefore be vulnerable to a reduction in local patient flows. Table 3 sets out in column B, for each hospital, the percentage of the expected utilisation rate that the residents of the hospital's home district actually take up.

104. A hospital whose prices are higher than those of its competitors is likely to be more vulnerable in the internal market. Hospitals' actual costs, including capital charges, but allowing for excess London costs and SIFTR, can be compared with expected values on the basis of actual activity, and national non-teaching hospital cost-per-case data at the specialty level. Those hospitals with costs most above the expected value may be more vulnerable, as purchasers become more price-sensitive. The ratio of actual to expected costs for the main inner London hospitals is set out in column C of Table 3.

105. In inner London most areas are within quick access of several hospitals. A greater degree of overlap between hospitals' access areas may indicate surplus provision. The size of the population for which a given hospital is the most accessible may be an indicator of its strategic viability, especially for local and emergency services. For each of the main acute hospitals in inner London, we looked at the surrounding area which was within a given level of accessibility in terms of time travelled by road transport, taking account of actual geographical circumstances. We commissioned plots of isochrones (the boundaries of these areas) for ten and fifteen minute access times. We assumed for this purpose that the new Westminster-Chelsea Hospital had already taken over from the old Westminster Hospital, and that current plans to close St Charles's Hospital had taken effect. The first of the two maps reproduced at the end of the report shows the ten minute isochrones for London's teaching hospitals and main DGHs. Even at this high level of accessibility, there is a great deal of overlap, especially in the central area.

106. Where populations (in terms of census enumeration districts) fell within more than one isochrone, we allocated them to the nearest hospital by distance, so that all enumeration districts were associated exclusively with one hospital: the most accessible. The second map shows the distribution of each hospital's "exclusive" population within its ten minute isochrone by plotting the enumeration districts in the same colour as the hospital's isochrone. In several cases the area of exclusive coverage is very much smaller even than the ten minute access area, and the exclusive population is correspondingly

small. The exclusive population relating to each of the main hospitals is shown in Table 3 column D. Column E of Table 3 draws together a combined score for each hospital, and ranks them in descending order of vulnerability.

107. Criteria such as those used in the above analysis are not so readily applicable to the SHAs. However the Department is examining the SHAs' business plans and the nature of patient flows for less specialised services. Their preliminary conclusion is that the Royal Brompton and the Royal Marsden are likely to be the most vulnerable in the internal market. Furthermore, the services provided by these hospitals, and by the National Hospital for Neurology and Neurosurgery are in specialties which we identify in paragraph 148 as needing early review and rationalisation.

TABLE 3

VULNERABILITY OF INNER LONDON HOSPITALS

Hospital	A (para 102)		B (para 103)		C (para 104)		D (para 105, 106)		E (para 106)	
	Use by non-local patients		Local use vs expected		Actual cost vs expected		Exclusive population		Total score	Over-all rank
	%	score	%	score	%	score	Number	score		
UCH	52	100	129	100	120	58	80153	81	339	1
Middlesex	52	100	129	100	108	19	80153	81	300	2
Bart's	30	41	100	37	129	87	34775	100	265	3
St Thomas's	31	43	100	37	124	71	84373	79	230	4
Royal London	27	32	108	54	116	45	139070	56	188	5
Charing Cross	23	22	83	0	133	100	115139	66	188	6
Guy's	22	19	94	24	108	19	75969	83	145	7
St Mary's	15	0	106	50	112	32	132380	59	141	8
Royal Free	23	22	94	24	107	16	144186	54	116	9
St George's	19	11	108	54	102	0	273042	0	65	10
King's	15	0	93	22	111	29	265723	3	54	11

Notes
1. Scores are generated by re-scaling percentage and population data on a scale from 0 - 100 (100 = most vulnerable). All scores are rounded; total scores are the sum of unrounded scores.
2. Columns A and B are based on DHA returns for 1990/91.
3. Column C is based on 1990/91 finance data for each hospital.
4. Column D is based on 1981 census enumeration district data.

Current financial pressures

108. Data such as those in Table 3 needs to be used carefully, and evaluated in the light of many other factors. However the relative positions of the hospitals, and their broad ranking, gives a helpful indication of where there may be problems in the future. Many of these hospitals are already in financial difficulty and are in receipt of transitional funding from the Thames

RHAs whilst they match their costs and activity to contracts. It is difficult to compare accurately the underlying financial position of trust and directly managed hospitals; and the success of each hospital in delivering cost savings this year remains to be seen. Even if they do achieve these savings, some units are projecting significant end-year deficits. At September 1992, and before transitional funding is taken into account, we understand that UCH-Middlesex had a forecast deficit of £18.5 million, St Bartholomew's £7 million, and Westminster-Charing Cross £6.4 million.

Buildings

109. Many hospitals have been spending heavily on refurbishment and new buildings, some of which developments have been supported by charitable funds. As far as possible, good buildings in strategic locations should be retained in NHS use, and poor, ill-sited, buildings should be abandoned. However such sunk costs, however recently incurred, are small compared to the revenue costs of the NHS; they should not dictate strategic development in London.

Hospitals where change is recommended

110. Our analysis of the vulnerability and natural catchments of the main inner London hospitals is fairly crude; and in any case, the interdependency of the hospitals is such that any recommendation for one will have major implications for the others. However the analysis suggests that there are several major hospitals which are at significant risk, and which ought therefore to be rationalised in order that the hospital service in inner London as a whole will be strengthened for the future. This group of hospitals at the top of our vulnerability ranking falls naturally into four pairs: University College and the Middlesex; St Bartholomew's and the Royal London; St Thomas's and Guy's; and (looking a few months ahead) Charing Cross and the new Westminster and Chelsea.

111. The following paragraphs set out the changes we recommend for the inner London hospitals (including SHAs) as soon as practically possible. These changes are not intended to deliver a level of bed reductions specifically calculated on the basis of our analysis of surplus beds, but they do start out in the direction indicated by that analysis, in the light of the present state of the hospitals. While we give our reasons for our recommendations, we do not set out all the alternatives that we have considered and discarded. Where there are options that we have not been able to choose between, we propose specific further work to determine the way forward. We do not comment here on hospitals for which we make no specific recommendations. However all hospitals will be affected by the pan-London review and rationalisation of specialties which we recommend in paragraph 150. All hospitals must be prepared to participate in this, and to give up some services, in exchange for others, where this is in the best interests of the service. In preparing our

recommendations, we have made a particular point of seeking a "bottom up" analysis from the individual institutions, and especially from the four RHAs.

112. As the process of change unfolds, as patient flows become clearer, and as developments in service delivery and efficiency take hold, further rationalisation is likely to be needed. It will fall to the Implementation Group to which we refer in paragraph 255 to identify the direction in which market forces are pointing, and to ensure that the necessary further changes are managed smoothly.

University College and Middlesex Hospitals

113. In our assessment of the main inner London hospitals, the combined unit of University College Hospital (UCH) and the Middlesex Hospital ranks highest in overall vulnerability. It is at greatest risk of losing non-local patients in the internal market: less than half of its referrals come from nearby districts. Its local population also appears to have the greatest excess use of acute services. UCH ranks fourth in terms of the level of excess costs (although the Middlesex part of the unit does better in this respect). The combined unit ranks third in terms of the smallness of the population for which it is the most accessible. It is in the most serious financial difficulty in the current year.

114. On the other hand, UCH-Middlesex supports one of the highest graded clinical research institutions in London. We recommend in paragraph 183 that the Royal Free and the University College and Middlesex medical schools should merge; once the SHAs at Queen Square and Great Ormond Street are integrated into the internal market, and their related postgraduate institutes work more closely with University College, this group of hospitals has the potential to be an important service and research centre. In addition, UCH is regarded by the London Ambulance Service as playing an important part in the A & E network in central London, and as having the best road access.

115. Previous plans for the redevelopment of UCH-Middlesex have already been shelved. If the excess costs of this unit are to be brought under control, it is clear that one of the two sites must be abandoned, and that a smaller unit should be located on the other. It is also necessary, in the light of our recommendations below on other hospitals, for an A & E service to be maintained on the remaining site. This therefore sets the strategic framework for the rationalisation of UCH-Middlesex.

116. In addition to the functions needed to support the A & E service, we would expect the rationalisation of specialties which we recommend in paragraph 150 to focus a small number of specialist services at this unit. These would link closely with the neighbouring services at the Royal Free and the Whittington, and with services and research in neurosciences (in which University College is already pre-eminent) and paediatrics at Queen Square and Great Ormond Street respectively. The objective should be to eliminate

duplication of specialties between the sites, and for all of them to be regarded as a group. Plans are already in hand for re-providing the distinctive service currently at the Elizabeth Garrett Anderson Hospital, at the main unit. Likewise, discussions are in progress on relocating the services of the Royal National Throat Nose and Ear Hospital, and the Hospital for Tropical Diseases within UCH-Middlesex. Factors such as these, and the requirements of local purchasers, will enable an early decision to be taken on the final size of the required unit.

117. We understand that current capital costings suggest that development of the Middlesex site would be the more economical option. However this would be an inferior option both from the point of view of A & E access, and from the point of view of greater inter-working with University College and with Queen Square and Great Ormond Street. Of the various options that have been put to us, we ***recommend*** that efforts should be made to find a cost-effective redevelopment of existing sites on the UCH campus.

St Bartholomew's and the Royal London Hospitals

118. Bart's ranks third in terms of use by non-local patients. However data are not available to allow our analysis to distinguish fully the patient flows to the two sites which comprise the Bart's unit: West Smithfield and Homerton. According to North East Thames RHA (NETRHA), Bart's gets 43% of its patients from City and Hackney DHA, and 24% from outside NETRHA. Homerton gets 80% of its work from City and Hackney. We therefore conclude that our analysis significantly understates the vulnerability of Bart's to the withdrawal of non-local flows.

119. City and Hackney residents do not show an excess use of acute services, and in any case, the district is expected to gain under weighted capitation. However Bart's ranks second in terms of its level of excess costs, and has the highest capital charges. Its estate comprises predominantly listed buildings, which limits the scope for development and rationalisation. It has by far the smallest exclusive population base - its ten minute isochrone is most overlapped by those of other hospitals. The unit is in severe recurrent financial difficulties, which are likely to penalise its associated hospital at Homerton. We do not believe there is a long-term future for a major hospital on the West Smithfield site.

120. The Royal London Hospital has a strong local patient base in a district which also gains under capitation. The apparent slight over-use of acute services by Tower Hamlets residents does not therefore indicate significant vulnerability on that score, although the Royal London does appear vulnerable in terms of its costs. There is, inevitably, duplication of services between the two hospitals, which does not enhance the position of either of them.

121. There is a long-standing need for rationalisation of services between the Royal London and Bart's, and for progress towards the full integration of

clinical undergraduate teaching. This would in turn improve opportunities for research and postgraduate teaching by creating a larger ''critical mass'' close to Queen Mary and Westfield College. We understand that discussions are in hand on both these subjects. We ***recommend*** that the City and east London area would be better served by a merged hospital bringing together the best of both institutions. This new merged hospital should be centred on the present Royal London site.

122. With the inevitable run-down of the West Smithfield site, we ***recommend*** that a single management unit be created to embrace St Bartholomew's and the Royal London. Accordingly, we ***recommend*** that the Bart's trust should not proceed as planned in April 1993. In line with our recommendation at paragraph 227, we ***recommend*** that this new management unit should not take full possession of the Smithfield site, but should be specifically charged with its orderly run-down and disposal.

123. The Homerton Hospital is well located in an area of high population. It provides important district general hospital services, and would continue to be a valuable research and teaching resource for the merged Bart's and Royal London medical school which we recommend later in this report. We ***recommend*** that it should form a separate and independent management unit, and should in due course be constituted as an NHS trust.

124. We are satisfied that full A & E services for the City of London area will be adequately provided by Guy's or St Thomas's, the Royal London and University College hospitals. There is no part of Bart's exclusive population area that is not overlapped by the ten minute isochrone of at least one of these hospitals. However this area of London, though sparsely populated, attracts a large number of daytime visitors. Following our recommendation in paragraph 47, we ***recommend*** that consideration be given to providing within the City of London an extended health centre on the lines of that planned for South Westminster. Part of the Smithfield site may be appropriate for this.

St Thomas's and Guy's Hospitals

125. Analyses of demand and purchasing intentions by South East Thames RHA (SETRHA) and South East London Commissioning Agency (SELCA) suggest that, of the four major hospitals serving SELCA (King's, Guy's, Lewisham and St Thomas's), at most only three will be required within the next five years. We agree with this assessment, and moreover we are satisfied that King's and Lewisham have a secure future. The question therefore is which of the hospitals on the South Bank should be retained. St Thomas's seems to be a little more vulnerable than Guy's to the withdrawal of distant patient flows, and a little less vulnerable in terms of exclusive population. The two are not significantly at risk in terms of excess local use, although St Thomas's does seem to be significantly more vulnerable in its costs. Overall, our analysis shows St Thomas's to be slightly more vulnerable

than Guy's, but of course, since the two are only just over a mile apart, the effect of the closure of one would outweigh any difference in their vulnerability.

126. St Thomas's building stock is on the whole of better quality than that of Guy's, and seems to be better suited to use as an integrated hospital. Guy's poorer estate has more than twice the level of backlog maintenance, and rather higher capital charges per bed. Guy's Phase III building will open in 1994, and will improve the average rating of its building stock, but it is not clear that this will directly enable any significant rationalisation of the estate, or reductions in costs. In terms of coverage for local services and A & E, our maps of access isochrones suggest that St Thomas's makes a significantly greater geographical contribution than does Guy's.

127. On the basis of all these considerations it might be better to close Guy's. However options have been put to us for the re-use of the St Thomas's estate within the health and medical education sector. The principal option is to use St Thomas's as an alternative to the development of Cornwall House as the centre for life sciences within King's College and the planned combined medical school of King's and UMDS. No such clear options have been proposed for Guy's, and in particular for its Phase III building, although a similar scheme might be equally applicable to Guy's.

128. SETRHA is undertaking further, more sensitive, analysis of the choice between the two sites. Its main focus is on the relative flexibility of the sites, the relative costs of reorganisation onto one of them, and the resulting redirection of patient flows. For the reasons given in paragraph 109 we do not regard one-off capital costs as decisive; we regard geographical coverage and patient accessibility as equally important. The choice of site seems to be finely balanced. In any case, once that decision has been made, we ***recommend*** that a single management structure for Guy's and St Thomas's should be created, with the specific task of rationalising services onto the chosen site. It should complete this work within two years.

129. It follows from the preceding paragraphs that in any case we ***recommend*** that the Guy's-Lewisham trust must be split, with Lewisham Hospital continuing as a separate trust, as it is well able to do.

Charing Cross Hospital

130. Charing Cross Hospital ranks about midway in our overall scale of vulnerability. The new Westminster-Chelsea Hospital already represents a significant rationalisation of hospital provision in west central London, but its opening in April 1993 will further impact on Charing Cross, and we therefore regard the latter as more vulnerable from then on. Charing Cross stands out as having the highest level of excess costs. The joint Westminster-Charing Cross unit is already running an expected current deficit of £6.4 million before transitional funding. North West Thames RHA (NWTRHA) and local

purchasers tell us that "district general" and A & E services could be provided at the new hospital, and at the Hammersmith. Our isochrone analysis confirms this. Charing Cross currently provides specialist services in cancer, nephrology, plastic surgery and neurosurgery. If the review of specialties showed that these were a necessary component of the overall volume of such services in London, they would need to be consolidated on the Charing Cross site, or re-provided elsewhere. Priority acute services (mental illness and elderly) for the local population are also provided within the Charing Cross building; if they too could be relocated, the entire site could be sold.

131. However the building is reasonably new and in good condition and if possible should continue in NHS use in preference to worse buildings elsewhere in the NHS estate. It is large enough, and sufficiently well provided with teaching and research facilities, to provide a new centre for some of the scattered specialist hospitals in London. For example, there could be significant benefits to cardiothoracic and cancer services if the Royal Brompton and Royal Marsden hospitals could be brought together on the Charing Cross site, along with the Institute for Cancer Research and the National Heart and Lung Institute. The existing cancer service at Charing Cross would merge with the Marsden's service. However this could still leave capacity at the Charing Cross building, which should be used to the full. Subject to the review of specialties, plastic surgery, nephrology and neurosciences might remain on the site, provided equivalent bed savings were made elsewhere to compensate. NWTRHA is examining a range of possibilities, which, in addition to specialist services, would include keeping priority services on the site, and providing primary care facilities to the local population.

132. Developments along these lines could create a major specialist centre which would be more than merely two single-specialty hospitals in one building. It would expand and consolidate the patient base and "critical mass" available for both undergraduate and postgraduate teaching, and for research, in the specialties brought together there. The present state of the property market makes it difficult to assess the balance in capital costs of such a move. However the sale of the SHA sites in Chelsea, would clearly make at least a major contribution to the direct costs of the moves. In addition, there would be revenue savings from a more efficient use of estate and from economies of scale.

133. Our preferred option, which we ***recommend***, is that the Royal Brompton and Royal Marsden hospitals be relocated to the Charing Cross building, alongside other services to ensure the full utilisation of the site. If this cannot be achieved, the Charing Cross site should be sold.

Royal Brompton Hospital

134. Cardiothoracic services are widely dispersed around London, and the Royal Brompton Hospital has to play its part in their reorganisation. The Brompton is isolated both academically and as a service unit, and is likely to be one of the SHAs most vulnerable to financial pressures if it is not integrated into a rationalised cardiothoracic service. Although it has recently had some new building, much of its estate is in poor condition. However it could form a key element of cardiothoracic services and research by moving to the Charing Cross building. We ***recommend*** that this should happen, and that the Chelsea site should be sold.

135. Although within the same management unit, the service and academic links between the Brompton and the London Chest Hospital (LCH) are tenuous. The LCH houses the biggest cardiac surgery unit in NE Thames, and is a major centre for angioplasty and the treatment of lung cancer and tuberculosis. It is not heavily involved in research, but deals with many cases from a deprived local population as well as considerable numbers from further afield. It serves the same population as the Royal London Hospital only one mile away, and for most practical purposes, the LCH links with that hospital, rather than its parent in Chelsea. We ***recommend*** that the review of cardiothoracic services should look for an opportunity to merge the London Chest into the Royal London. It follows that the LCH should be managerially separated from the Brompton, and in due course it might be possible for the LCH site to be sold.

Royal Marsden Hospital

136. The Marsden is similarly isolated and vulnerable, and likewise cancer services are dispersed around London. As above, we ***recommend*** that the Marsden's services on the Chelsea site should form the basis of an integrated and rationalised west London cancer service, at the Charing Cross building. The Chelsea site should be sold. The Marsden's management have argued that the Sutton unit forms, with the Marsden, part of an integrated service and research entity. We ***recommend*** that these services should remain as presently organised, but that both units should be included in the review of cancer services which we recommend in paragraph 150.

St Mary's Hospital

137. St Mary's ranks fairly low in our assessment of vulnerability. Its current financial position is stable. However decisions must be taken soon on its development, for which proposals are outstanding. Current plans for the development of the St Mary's site need to be re-appraised, although the objective of closing and re-providing the acute services at St Charles, together with the Samaritan and Western Ophthalmic units is sound. Overall, this sector of London will require less bed capacity, and we believe that this

should be achieved by a further reduction in the planned size of St Mary's. Considerable capital could be released by selling some poor quality buildings to British Rail, and undertaking a much more modest development so as merely to enable any necessary re-provision of services following the review of London specialties. Accordingly, we ***recommend*** that the St Mary's trust should go ahead as planned in April 1993, but on the basis of a reduced number of beds. Further consideration will need to be given to the proportion of the estate which is transferred to the trust, in line with our general recommendation in paragraph 227.

The Hospitals for Sick Children

138. We have referred to the need for closer links between Great Ormond Street (GOS) and the Institute of Child Health, UCH and University College, and we are glad to see that these are developing. However we are not convinced that it is necessary or appropriate for the associated hospital, Queen Elizabeth Hospital for Children (QEH) in Hackney, to remain within the same management unit as GOS. QEH provides a district general paediatric service to the same population as that to which the Homerton Hospital provides other general acute services (including some paediatric services). We consider that there are benefits to be gained from a fully integrated district service. Accordingly, we ***recommend*** that QEH should be managerially integrated into the proposed Homerton trust, and that an opportunity should be sought for the re-provision of its services on the Homerton site in due course.

139. The Institute of Child Health is developing valuable research initiatives in conjunction with QEH, where the patient population presents opportunities not available at GOS. In addition, the two units at GOS and QEH offer complementary training experience both for junior doctors and for nurses. It is essential that these academic and training links be maintained.

Hammersmith and Queen Charlotte's Hospitals

140. The Hammersmith Hospital provides a local service to a defined area, while pursuing high quality research and teaching in a range of specialties. Its detailed portfolio of services should be included within the pan-London review and rationalisation of specialties which we propose in paragraph 150. However we understand that the Queen Charlotte Hospital maternity service is barely cost-effective at its present volume, and therefore ***recommend*** that consideration be given to providing these services elsewhere, mainly at neighbouring maternity units within NWTRHA, and at the Hammersmith site because of research links, allowing the Queen Charlotte site to be sold.

Moorfields Eye Hospital

141. Moorfields has put to us an imaginative proposal for the development of all ophthalmology services north of the River Thames. This is based upon the multi-disciplinary approach they have developed, providing a largely

ambulatory ophthalmic service. Although in general we believe that small single-specialty hospitals are undesirable, this seems less the case where the great majority of cases are not admitted as inpatients. We ***recommend*** that the implications of this scheme be tested with purchasers in the North Thames regions, paying particular attention to the risk of creating a monopoly.

Royal National Throat Nose and Ear Hospital

142. This trust is in some financial difficulty, and its continued separate existence as a single-specialty service is not sustainable. It is already closely linked with University College through the Institute of Otology and Laryngology, and discussions are under way with UCH-Middlesex to merge ENT services. We ***recommend*** that this merger into the re-developed University College Hospital should go ahead as quickly as possible, the trust should be dissolved, and its site sold.

St Mark's Hospital

143. This is a small specialist unit which gets the great majority of its patients from outside NETRHA. Its premises are barely fit for continued use, and the isolation of the unit makes no financial, service or academic sense. However it provides specialist services and research support which ought to be preserved within a larger organisation. St Mark's is currently the responsibility of City and Hackney DHA, and was planned to move into the West Smithfield site as part of the proposed Bart's trust. However we do not consider that any services should move into Smithfield, and we support proposals from St Mark's itself that it should move elsewhere, with Northwick Park being the preferred location. We ***recommend*** that this plan be pursued with all speed, and that the services concerned be integrated as soon as possible into a larger general hospital outside central London. The site in City Road should be sold.

Hospital for Tropical Diseases

144. This is a small isolated unit of around 35 beds, housed in poor buildings. However it is the diagnostic, treatment and clinical teaching and research centre of the School of Hygiene and Tropical Medicine, which stands close to University College and UCH. We ***recommend*** that the hospital should be merged with the redeveloped UCH as quickly as possible, and its site sold.

Rationalisation of services

145. The changes we have set out above create a framework of hospital sites which should be viable in the short- and medium-term. Within this framework there needs to be a wholesale rationalisation of services, in particular

specialised services, across London. The actual number of open and closed beds varies from time to time, as does the use to which they are put (acute, ''local acute'', non-acute, etc). This makes it difficult to estimate the effects of the changes we propose in terms of actual productive acute capacity. However as a broad indication, the closures and mergers we recommend, together with other changes already planned by the RHAs (including the opening of the Westminster-Chelsea Hospital) result in a reduction in gross capacity of around 4200 beds. Within this total, around 1700 beds are currently closed, so that the net reduction in productive capacity would be around 2500 beds. The utilisation of the remaining bed capacity needs to be planned in detail. Plans for decanting specific services from a site that is to close must clearly be informed by a pan-London review of those services. However it is important that such consideration of the disposition of individual services should not delay the strategic decisions on the future of hospital sites.

146. We have referred in paragraph 87 to the need for the SHA hospitals to be brought into the internal market, and to the distortion of weighted capitation caused by their existence as a free good. This is likely to result in a need for fewer beds in the SHAs. Moreover, the present funding of the SHAs represents ''unfair'' competition with other providers, which could cause the collapse of hospitals for which there may be a greater strategic need. For all these reasons, we ***recommend*** that the SHAs' service capacity must be included in the rationalisation of acute sector capacity in London.

147. The majority of the SHAs are single specialty hospitals. This is not the ideal way to provide best patient care, although all the SHAs set themselves high standards. Their inability to share common facilities with other units reduces cost-effectiveness. Ideally, each SHA should be part of a major hospital complex, thus reducing their isolation from other specialties, and from other research interests. Opportunities should be taken as they arise to achieve this objective, whilst allowing the SHAs and institutes to retain their distinctive features. We have identified above some early possibilities for relocation.

148. It is clear that there is unwarranted duplication of specialist services, sometimes at great expense. It is plainly inefficient, and not conducive to good patient care, that there should be handfuls of beds in a single specialty, scattered between units less than a mile or two apart. For example, the Thames RHAs have reported to us that the number of centres, including the SHAs, providing regional specialties in inner London are 14 in cardiac services, 13 in cancer services, 13 in neurosciences, 11 in renal services, and 9 in plastic surgery.

149. This duplication of services is in part caused by the general lack of consistent pan-London planning, to which we refer in paragraph 253. However it is also attributable to two other factors: the close identity between each medical school and ''its'' hospital, which leads to pressure to have all specialties in every hospital; and the well-intentioned efforts of the special

trustees of the teaching hospitals and SHAs who are able to marshal sometimes huge wealth in support of priorities which may not always accord with the health needs of the population. We make a recommendation on the first of these points in paragraph 186. On the second point, while charitable donations are to be welcomed, we ***recommend*** that any service development using charitable money should be subject to formal approval by the relevant purchasers on a pan-London basis.

150. We have met much agreement on the need for rationalisation of specialties amongst those we have met, and have been sent detailed proposals from several quarters. We are in no doubt as to the benefits for patients (in terms of improved service quality) and for education and research (in terms of greater "critical mass") to be gained from the rationalisation and re-grouping of services in this way. We ***recommend*** that working parties be formed, under the direction of the Implementation Group to which we refer in paragraph 255, to review each specialty. Each working party would make recommendations for the capacity required to serve the demand likely to arise, and for the disposition of this capacity within the London hospitals in an efficient, effective and economical manner. These working parties should start with the duplicated specialties mentioned in paragraph 148 above. It has also been reported to us that orthopaedics, paediatric surgery and neo-natal intensive care are under-provided in some areas. These specialties should also be a high priority for review.

151. The specialty review working parties should comprise senior specialists, both from the NHS and from academic medicine, together with managers of relevant experience. Their composition should be weighted towards non-Londoners, and towards purchasers. Each working party should be required to complete its work within six months, and all specialties should be reviewed in as short a time as possible.

Accident and emergency services

152. The disposition of hospital sites which we recommend is, in our opinion, and in the assessment of the RHAs, quite adequate to provide good access to A & E services. The new systems being introduced by the London Ambulance Service will enable them to adapt readily to this revised network of A & E sites. Full A & E services need to be provided in hospitals offering the normal range of district general hospital specialties - orthopaedics, general surgery, general medicine, cardiology, paediatrics. The reviews of specialty services referred to above will therefore need to take account of this inter-relationship.

153. However the type of A & E provision required is likely to vary across the capital according to both local and pan-London strategic needs. It is apparent that the traditional model of A & E services does not offer sufficient flexibility to cope with the varying demands in the capital. These range from dealing with major disasters with enhanced specialty back up in "trauma

centres'', through to small community-based and primary care led units able to refer where necessary to nearby acute hospitals. We make recommendations in paragraph 47 on the ways in which A & E services could be adapted to meet more effectively the ''primary'' end of the spectrum. We understand that the Department is sponsoring an evaluation of the Stoke-on-Trent Trauma Centre and the results of this, when available, should be translated to a pan-London context.

Closed beds

154. There are already acute beds closed in almost every hospital in inner London. Temporary bed closures are an essential part of management, as wards need to be closed for reorganisation or refurbishment; or following an outbreak of infection. Indeed, the NHS internal market will work most effectively when there is a small surplus of hospital capacity available in the form of closed beds. The number of closed beds at any one time is hard to calculate, since, for the reasons above, it is constantly changing. However the Thames RHAs estimate that between 10% and 15% of acute beds in inner London hospitals are ''temporarily closed'' at any time. Equivalent statistics for the rest of the country are not available for comparison, but we consider that this may be an excessive proportion. If an ''appropriate'' incidence of temporary closure were taken as the equivalent of every hospital closing one ward for six months of the year, the average proportion of closed beds would be nearer 2%. On this basis, around 1000 beds in inner London could currently be judged ''inappropriately'' closed. Maintaining an excessive level of temporarily closed beds represents needless inefficiency, which our recommendations for rationalisation should help to reduce.

Location of acute services

155. Our recommendations so far have been concerned with reducing the growing over-capacity in London. The four Thames RHAs have satisfied us that, over all, there is no corresponding under-capacity in the non-London areas of their regions. Indeed it is possible that, even after unnecessary referrals into London have ceased, there will be surplus capacity in outer London and beyond. It will be necessary to keep this under review, to ensure that any developments there are soundly based.

156. Beyond that, however, there is a further option to move some hospital services out of the high-cost inner London area. Despite the possible financial benefits, we believe that all patients should have reasonable access to routine, or ''local'', services. In any case, A & E cover must be provided for every area, and this is most economically sited alongside a ''core business'' of key specialties. Highly specialised services, on the other hand, should be concentrated in the most appropriate centres, alongside other hospital facilities, whether in or out of London.

FUNDING THE SPECIAL HEALTH AUTHORITIES

157. Single-specialty hospitals are, on the whole, less than ideal for patient care, and for research and teaching. The isolation of the Special Health Authorities is counter-productive. It has been sustained by, and probably would have collapsed without, their separate central funding by the Department of Health. We have referred in paragraphs 87 and 146 to the distortions in the supply side of the internal market, and in fair weighted capitation funding, which the present arrangements cause. Hospital capacity across London needs to be brought into balance with demand as soon as possible, and the SHAs should be included in an urgent and wholesale review of service disposition and capacity. The SHAs are inseparable, in this respect, from other specialist service units across London.

158. Other hospitals which support research and teaching receive additional funding through SIFTR to cover the excess costs incurred in service provision due to academic activity. We have considered whether, in the case of the SHAs, their service overheads require more, or different, funding than in the case of other hospitals. We recommend in paragraph 207 that the postgraduate institutes associated with the SHAs should eventually be linked, together with the undergraduate medical schools, into the faculties of medicine of the four multi-faculty colleges of London University. We do not think it would make sense for the service support for research and teaching carried out under the aegis of one medical faculty to be funded in different ways.

159. The postgraduate institutes have suggested to us that patient services are an integral part of the costs of research, and thus should be wholly centrally funded, without recourse to the internal market. They argue that requiring patient flows to be secured in the internal market, even at a generously subsidised price, would place at risk the continuity and quality of research. Although full central funding as a "free good" would diminish the equity and flexibility which weighted capitation and the internal market seek to foster, they propose that stable, high quality research is the greater national priority.

160. We recognise the concerns expressed by the postgraduate schools. But three-quarters of all university clinical research is carried out in institutions other than the postgraduate schools, and relies upon patients in hospitals supported by SIFTR. This regime enables them to carry on research and teaching on a patient base secured at a fair price in the NHS market. Nor is full central funding necessary for high quality in research: the majority of institutions with above-average Universities Funding Council (UFC) ratings for clinical research are linked to hospitals funded in the NHS market, with SIFTR.

161. These facts confirm our conclusion that both the patient service and research overhead funding of the SHAs should be opened to competition. We

therefore ***recommend*** that the present SHAs should join the internal market for patient services, while their service overheads incurred in research and teaching should be subsidised by a reformed SIFTR. The natural consequence for the governance of the present SHAs would be that they should become NHS trusts. We make further recommendations below about support for special cases where a SIFTR-style supplement may be inadequate.

162. We see no reason to create a new system for meeting the service overheads of hospitals used for research and teaching by universities (in the case of research, either for university-funded projects or for projects funded by external bodies through universities). We note that while the primary role of the SHAs is to support research, they also support a substantial amount of postgraduate teaching leading to university qualifications. These links will be reinforced by our recommendations on integrating the postgraduate schools and institutes within the multi-faculty colleges of London University, and increasing their contribution to undergraduate teaching in line with the recommendations of the GMC for a ''core plus options'' curriculum.

163. We therefore ***recommend*** that a single system be developed, building on the current SIFTR, covering undergraduate teaching hospitals and the present SHAs. This would place the present SHAs on a level playing-field with other hospitals carrying out research and teaching. The main principles underlying this development of SIFTR should be:

a. funding should be available for the excess service costs of academic teaching and of peer-reviewed research. We believe it is essential to sustain the freedom of universities to pursue their research priorities within this framework. External peer review and academic validation will provide the necessary quality control. As in the present SIFTR, there would be no factor for the training of junior doctors, which takes place in all hospitals and is being dealt with separately by the Department of Health;

b. the formula for allocating funds to regions should deal separately with research and teaching. If the present SIFTR review does not achieve this, an empirical basis for distributing funds should be devised using measures of peer-reviewed research activity. RHAs should build on their current work to take separate account of research and teaching in funding for units. (During the SHAs' transition to this new regime, allocations to SHAs would be made centrally, rather than by RHAs);

c. the level of service increment would need to reflect the volume of patient flows needed to support the hospital's research programme. While the details of sub-regional allocation are a matter for RHAs in consultation with universities and research interests, we consider that it is important that fixed infrastructural costs are taken into account as well as the identifiable additional costs of research and teaching.

164. Once the service rationalisation recommended in paragraph 150 is complete, there will still be substantial and concentrated volumes of service in each specialty in London, and this will be available to support the research currently supported by the SHAs. These services will be sustained by NHS contracts in the internal market, together with support for excess costs. The ''natural catchment'' populations served by these services, under contract from the NHS commissioning authorities, will generate most of the cases needed to support research without difficulty.

165. However special provision needs to be made for research which requires more cases to be brought together in one hospital than a ''natural catchment'' population could be expected to generate. If such rare conditions are to be the subject of research, special contracts, akin to those for supra-regional services, will need to be placed for the services related to them, in order to ensure adequate and stable patient flows. By their nature, services secured in this way would have a small impact on the equity of capitation funding, and on commissioning authorities' purchasing autonomy. Research teams and their associated hospitals would, as part of the research planning process, bid for such central support.

166. We therefore ***recommend*** that central arrangements be made for identifying and funding through special contracts those relatively few rare cases that need, in the interests of worthwhile research, to be brought together in one (or more than one) specified hospital. Usually, there will be strong service reasons (in terms of quality and efficiency) for concentrating such activity. However where research interest is the only reason for a referral to be made under such a central contract, we ***recommend*** that, for ethical reasons, the patient's consent to the referral should be obtained.

167. Transitional measures will be needed to enable the level playing-field to be established without excessive disruption, as the present SHAs change and develop their organisations to meet these new opportunities. However in the longer term, there should be no presumption that the regime we describe would be restricted only to the institutions currently constituted as the eight SHAs. We ***recommend*** that this regime should be available to any partnership of research and service institutions, anywhere in the country, which offer a research programme of sufficient quality.

ORGANISATION OF PURCHASING AUTHORITIES

168. All the changes and developments we have recommended in the primary, community and acute sectors will need to be backed by strong and effective purchasers. Assessment of population health needs, and commissioning services for maximum health gain, are new skills for NHS staff. It is vital that purchasers are in the forefront in planning change, so that provider and professional dominance in the NHS do not reassert themselves. We ***recommend*** that additional resources be devoted to the development of the purchasing function in London, and that the consolidation of purchasing authorities into groups serving populations of between 500,000 to 750,000 should continue. As we have said in paragraph 71, locality-based purchasing should be developed where more than one local authority is within a purchaser's boundary.

169. Many of the DHA boundaries in London were originally defined in order to encompass a specific hospital or group of hospitals, so as to facilitate rational planning of services between the sites involved. While there is now no less need for such rationalisation, many district boundaries are no longer relevant, and, in their interaction with FHSA and London Borough boundaries, are in fact an obstacle to effective service planning and commissioning.

170. We have noted elsewhere our approval of the moves towards greater inter-working between DHAs, or consortia of DHAs, and their corresponding FHSAs. We are also concerned that this cooperation within the health service should be easily extendable to the local authorities in the planning of care in the community from April 1993. We ***recommend*** that the NHS commissioning authorities for HCHS and FHS should be coterminous; and that their common boundary should exclusively embrace one or more London Boroughs.

171. We have been impressed by the ability and dedication of all the NHS staff we have met. However we note that there is a marked difference in the value which the system seems to place upon FHSA and CHS managers, at one end of the scale, and hospital managers, at the other, with DHA purchasers perhaps in between. We doubt whether the balance between the commissioners and providers of health services will be optimal while "weight", kudos, and financial reward are so unevenly distributed. We ***recommend*** that a fairer balance of reward be found, bearing in mind the increasing amount of patient care taking place in the community.

EDUCATION AND RESEARCH

MEDICAL EDUCATION AND RESEARCH

172. The NHS reforms will have a major impact on London medical schools. But changes in the pattern and organisation of teaching and research should enable London to maintain and reinforce its status as a major national and international medical centre.

173. London currently accounts for some 30% of the pre-clinical intake to all medical schools, and for around a third of clinical undergraduates because of transfers, mainly from Oxford and Cambridge. We have received no convincing evidence to show that the quality of medical teaching in London is better or worse than elsewhere. The average A-level score of entrants to London medical schools is similar to that of medical undergraduates elsewhere. There is evidence that demand for London places is somewhat above average, while work by Department for Education economists suggests that completion rates may be marginally lower. London students we have met have expressed loyalty to and satisfaction with their medical schools, although costs and time for travel to peripheral hospitals are a concern.

174. London accounts for over half of university clinical research income, and its medical schools have high levels of research income per academic. However, of the nine London undergraduate schools only University College achieved an above-average rating for clinical medicine in the UFC's most recent (1989) research assessment exercise. Six of the seven undergraduate schools which achieved such ratings were outside London. All three of the London postgraduate medical schools achieved above-average ratings, but with significant variations between individual institutes of the British Postgraduate Medical Federation (BPMF). This evidence suggests that there is no necessary link between research quality and levels of research income.

175. Higher education in London is more expensive than elsewhere. In addition to the UFC's standard funding, London University will receive some £65 million in special factor funding in 1992/93. The largest part of this is for London weighting, with most of the remainder to support particular institutions within London (including postgraduate medical schools) and for the extra costs of the federal University. In aggregate this special factor funding adds around 18% to basic teaching and research costs.

176. Data produced by the Committee of Vice-Chancellors and Principals (CVCP) and the UFC for 1990-91 show that student-staff ratios for clinical medicine in London were 22% lower than the UK average. The same data suggest that the unit cost to the university of teaching students in clinical medicine in London is some 15% above average, excluding non-departmental costs which are also higher in London. NHS funding through SIFTR is 9% higher in London.

Organisation of undergraduate medical schools

177. We use "undergraduate" to describe those medical schools and faculties which teach undergraduate students. Such schools also teach post-graduate students and undertake research: the term is used simply as a convenient shorthand.

178. Historically London medical schools have been largely free-standing. They have not been, and still largely are not, part of multi-faculty institutions as is the case elsewhere. The nine undergraduate schools presently in existence are the product of a number of mergers in the past. We believe that a range of pressures require this process to be taken further.

179. Changes in UFC funding have led to pressures for more efficiency in teaching. As far as we can judge, no free-standing London medical school is currently at serious financial risk as a result. But these changes have increased the need to rationalise resources, and to remove duplication of posts. The CVCP/UFC data show that the multi-faculty institutions of King's and University Colleges already have unit costs for clinical medicine significantly below the London average. The UFC's decision to introduce direct funding of the major multi-faculty colleges from 1992/93 will further underline the isolation of the free-standing medical schools.

180. Changes proposed by the GMC to the curriculum require more integration of clinical and basic science teaching and development of a range of options for students to take beyond their core studies. There are academic and financial diseconomies in free-standing medical schools seeking to deliver the full range of options for students. London University has already recognised this by moving towards academic clusters for teaching.

181. The move towards greater selectivity in UFC research funding has provided a major incentive to strengthen research. This involves creating links between clinical and basic science departments, and concentrating both pre-clinical and clinical research on fewer sites. The rationalisation of specialties which we proposed earlier in this report will provide a powerful mechanism for concentrating clinical research.

182. In principle, the benefits of cooperation and concentration of resources could be achieved through effective voluntary links. But the experience of London University in the 1980s shows that academic integration and rationalisation are most effectively carried out through unified medical faculties within multi-faculty colleges, with clear central aims and planning. We have noted that Bart's and the Royal London medical schools are part of a confederation with Queen Mary and Westfield College, but this seems little more than a paper exercise at clinical level, with minimal sharing of staff and facilities, and thus yielding few benefits. We do not believe that this is a desirable model.

183. We therefore ***recommend*** the merger of all but one of the present nine undergraduate medical schools into four faculties of medicine within the multi-faculty colleges of the University which teach medicine: University College, Imperial College, King's College and Queen Mary and Westfield College. Three of the nine medical schools - King's, St Mary's and University College and Middlesex - are already part of multi-faculty colleges. Our merger proposals are shown in Table 4.

184. St George's medical school is the only exception, because of its location well outside central London, and the absence of a nearby multi-faculty college with strong basic science. We note that it has well-developed plans for avoiding academic isolation, and has a strategy of expanding teaching in subjects allied to medicine and forming links with other higher education institutions in south London. But we ***recommend*** that, in the longer-term, St George's should aim for a merger with one of these institutions if it develops a life sciences base with appropriate strength in teaching and research.

TABLE 4

MERGERS OF UNDERGRADUATE MEDICAL SCHOOLS

Multi-faculty college	Constituent medical schools
Imperial College	St Mary's Westminster-Charing Cross
King's College	King's UMDS
Queen Mary and Westfield College	Royal London St Bartholomew's
University College	University College-Middlesex Royal Free

185. In order to achieve the desired academic and financial benefits, it is essential that these mergers are real and not cosmetic. We ***recommend*** that the new institutions should have a single administrative and financial structure, and should remove any academic duplication, particularly of clinical posts. They should also aim to rationalise their physical assets. The evidence of the reorganisation of London medical education after the Flowers Report is that genuine rationalisation produces both academic and financial benefits. But management commitment to change is essential to see this through. We have discussed this approach with the schools and with representatives of the University, and have found widespread - though not universal - acceptance that this is the right direction for the future.

Location of teaching and research

186. These merger proposals relate only to London medical schools. They do not imply that the hospitals currently linked with them should be maintained. We approve the increasing linkage of London's medical schools to more than one hospital for teaching, and ***recommend*** that they should build on existing trends to take advantage of the best clinical teaching opportunities available, irrespective of location. In order to maintain the academic involvement required, particularly for the early years of clinical teaching, it will be necessary to move some academic units into general hospitals. These should as far as possible be accessible to the medical school and to the multi-faculty base. For example, under this approach much of the current teaching at UCH-Middlesex might be moved to the Royal Free and the Whittington; while that at Bart's could move to Homerton and the Royal London as part of a merged school.

187. It is important that integration into multi-faculty schools does not reduce the scope for early clinical experience which the GMC is promoting through its planned new curriculum. We believe that, as long as the transitional period which we propose below is allowed for, there is no reason why early clinical experience should not be organised and built into the curriculum of the medical faculties of all the colleges.

188. While it is possible to disperse clinical teaching, we have indicated that clinical research needs to be strengthened by further concentration. This will involve moving laboratories and other facilities for clinical research into selected hospitals, as far as possible close to a basic science base. This process will need to proceed together with the programme of hospital rationalisation we propose earlier in the report.

Teaching in the community

189. The preceding analysis has been mainly concerned with the implications for medical schools of changes in the acute sector, where the pressures are most immediate. But in the future the development of teaching in primary and community care settings will be of equal or greater importance. In London, less than 5% of students' time is spent learning in a general practice. Recent studies, including those of the King's Fund, have emphasised the importance of this shift and the need to develop new community-based approaches to teaching. The GMC's proposed curriculum gives increased emphasis to teaching in general practice and the community. This will increasingly cover teaching in a broad range of clinical skills extending beyond general practice and community care.

190. It will not be easy to increase the amount of undergraduate teaching in general practice in London, for reasons we have already mentioned. We ***recommend*** that urgent consideration be given to including general practice within the scope of SIFTR, or to the creation of a parallel mechanism for

general practice. We further ***recommend*** that the improvements to GP and community care premises which we propose earlier in this report should take account of the need for teaching facilities. We refer below to the needs of GPs for postgraduate and continuing medical education, which will be essential to equip a wide range of GPs in London to teach. While the potential supply of GPs for teaching undergraduates in London is large, we do not believe that it is realistic to expect that these essential improvements can be brought about quickly.

Medical student numbers

191. The GMC were not in a position to provide advice on the numbers of beds or catchment population required for teaching, nor have they produced public assessments of the quality of teaching in individual institutions. In any case, the London medical schools have mostly argued that measures such as bed numbers are no longer relevant, as more teaching takes place in outpatients, and is moved into primary care and into peripheral hospitals. We accept that no simple means exists to measure the educational viability of particular medical schools against the background of changes in the NHS.

192. Nonetheless, we are concerned about the potential effects of changes in the NHS on the availability of facilities for medical teaching in London, and on their quality. In particular, we have noted that the base for teaching in primary care is weak; while extensive use of peripheral hospitals may reduce quality unless proper quality control arrangements are put in place, as well as imposing costs in time and money on students. Although the impact of changing patient flows affects other medical schools in inner city areas, the concentration of medical teaching in inner London and the weakness of the primary care base present particular problems there.

193. To meet educational needs, the number of students enrolled at London medical schools must be such that all students can receive good teaching in general practice and community settings, and spend a large part of their clinical training in hospitals with a sound patient base and a significant academic presence, particularly in the early clinical years. The latter need not be - and in some cases will not be - the teaching hospitals traditionally linked to each medical school. But it would not be desirable for clinical teaching to take place in hospitals or general practices with no academic links or quality control.

194. We have not sought to recommend changes in medical student numbers in London for their own sake. However reduced patient flows into inner London, and the difficulties of increasing teaching in primary care, are likely to make it more difficult to teach the present level of intake. The process of relocating clinical academic units further from the multi-faculty base and medical school cannot continue indefinitely without damaging academic links. We have doubts about the practicality of increasing the low proportion of

teaching in the community in London substantially in the near future, while maintaining quality.

195. The merged medical schools we propose for London will have significantly larger intakes. The view expressed to us by the heads of some London medical schools and multi-faculty colleges is that an intake of more than 200-250 students is undesirable in terms of the optimum organisation and management of teaching.

196. Taking account of this view, together with our conclusions on teaching hospital viability and the problems of increasing the amount of teaching in the community, we believe that a reduction of around 150 in the intake of medical students to London will be needed. We ***recommend*** that the HEFCE implement this through its distribution of the national quota for medicine, taking account of the need to phase changes so as to minimise the disruption faced by individual students and schools.

197. We recognise that the Medical Manpower Standing Advisory Committee chaired by Professor Colin Campbell will be reporting shortly after us. We believe the logic of our recommendations for London medical education points to reductions in student numbers in London, irrespective of the conclusions of the Committee. If the Committee were to recommend an increase in the total intake to medical schools, we ***recommend*** that it should take place outside London. As long as the total intake is not cut, places moved from London should be absorbed within spare capacity in provincial medical schools. A survey of medical schools by the UFC has indicated that spare capacity of 390 clinical places exists outside London without any additional capital expenditure.

Relocating a medical school

198. We have considered the possibility of moving a medical school, to outer London or outside London altogether. The rationale for this is that the initial capital outlay would be repaid in the long-term by savings on recurrent costs.

199. We do not believe that close academic links are sustainable if the distance between a multi-faculty institution and a medical school is too large. For that reason we do not believe that St George's medical school should be merged with a multi-faculty institution in central London. By the same token, it would not make academic sense to move a medical school, away from its multi-faculty college, to outer London. Increased use of peripheral teaching hospitals and primary care is already taking place. But we do not see any academic case for wholesale relocation to outer London.

200. Relocating a medical school outside London would, given the framework we have described above, require creation of a new medical school within a provincial university with strong basic sciences. This would not be

a ''move'' from London in a meaningful sense, since the school's traditional links would be severed and many staff might choose not to move. As we have explained, the reduction in student numbers in London which will be required can be absorbed within existing spare capacity in provincial medical schools, rather than by creation of a completely new school.

Postgraduate schools

201. London University has three postgraduate medical schools, of which one, the BPMF - is a federation of eight independent institutes. The schools and institutes vary considerably in size and in their research ratings. But together they have an honourable place in the history of teaching and research in British medicine, and in its present practice. Their location in London gives them a large population base and major opportunities for collaboration with the many basic science and clinical research centres there.

202. We strongly approve of the recent introduction of peer review by the BPMF, and of the greater selectivity in its internal distribution of funding to its institutes. This has led to considerable efforts to coordinate and monitor the activities of the institutes, and to extend collaboration with other parts of the University. We believe that the academic-led hospital model of the Royal Postgraduate Medical School (RPMS) and Hammersmith Hospital has been successful in linking research and service needs, and could have wider application elsewhere within a multi-faculty framework. We note the success of the RPMS in strengthening its basic science base by attracting a large part of the Medical Research Council's (MRC) Clinical Research Initiative. We have also been impressed by the breadth and quality of research at the London School of Hygiene and Tropical Medicine.

203. We want to see the research capacity of the postgraduate schools and institutes, which is the primary purpose of their existence, reach its full potential. Despite the progress which has been made in recent years, we do not believe that this will be realised as long as they remain self-standing, mainly single-specialty units separated from the regular contact, intellectual stimulus and facilities of the multi-faculty colleges of the University. The existence of separate postgraduate schools is peculiar to London: elsewhere high-quality research is carried out in the medical faculty of the university. The move to direct funding by the UFC of the major London colleges will leave the smaller schools and institutes outside them increasingly isolated.

204. We have already noted that clinical research will increasingly need to be concentrated on fewer sites, with close links to a basic science base. This concentration will be furthered by the rationalisation of specialties which we propose in this report. Increasingly it will make less sense, both for research and service, to maintain a number of separate single-specialty clinical research centres in London. Even so, it has been put to us that there is a case for retaining the postgraduate schools and institutes as independent entities, separate from issues about the merits of free-standing undergraduate schools.

There is strong concern among the postgraduate schools that they would require ring-fencing to survive in a multi-faculty environment, and that research priorities would be altered by integration into a faculty of medicine.

205. We have considered these arguments carefully, but we have not found them ultimately persuasive. We believe that the research potential of all the postgraduate schools, including those which are already strong, can only be fully realised through integration in multi-faculty colleges. Research selectivity gives all universities a strong incentive to sustain the best research. There is no reason why high quality research institutes should not prosper in this framework. There are significant academic and financial benefits to be realised by greater concentration of resources, but these can only be achieved through unified management. We do not believe that voluntary cooperation alone will achieve the full benefits. Moving to a multi-faculty framework would mean that the federal BPMF ceased to exist.

206. However, despite these arguments of principle, we believe there are practical difficulties with merging the postgraduate schools into the multi-faculty colleges in the near future. It is plain that the postgraduate schools are all, in various ways, reducing their isolation and forging closer links with other schools. This should in time lead to full mergers. Nonetheless, there is much less acceptance of the need for a multi-faculty framework among the postgraduate than the undergraduate schools, and the cultural and organisational changes required are greater. The multi-faculty colleges themselves have indicated that they do not wish to undertake this at the same time as mergers with undergraduate medical schools. It is likely that attempting to do so would damage both the colleges and the postgraduate schools.

207. We have therefore sought to establish a development path which would lead to the eventual establishment of the multi-faculty framework which we favour. We ***recommend*** that the aim should be the linkages set out in Table 5, and in the meantime:

a. the present moves to increase linkages between postgraduate schools and institutes and the rest of the University should be reinforced. While preserving their distinctive missions, the postgraduate schools should seek ways of making a greater contribution to undergraduate teaching in specialist areas as part of the GMC's new core plus options curriculum;

b. until such time as a multi-faculty framework is implemented, the BPMF should continue and build on its existing work in assessing and coordinating research;

c. the HEFCE should maintain the UFC's position of not providing direct funding for free-standing medical schools, which is undesirable in principle; but

d. the HEFCE should provide earmarked funding for postgraduate schools and institutes which seek it, provided that this is routed through a multi-faculty school which already has direct funding and which supports such an arrangement. This need not involve mergers, but will reinforce closer links; and

e. consideration should be given to the establishment within multi-faculty institutions of graduate schools covering a range of science disciplines, into which individual postgraduate medical schools and institutes could be integrated. This offers a means of concentrating research strength, while meeting the distinctive requirements of postgraduate education.

TABLE 5

MULTI-FACULTY COLLEGES AND POSTGRADUATE INSTITUTIONS

Multi-faculty college	Constituent postgraduate schools/institutes
Imperial College	Cancer Research
	National Heart & Lung
	Royal Postgraduate
King's College	Psychiatry
University College	Child Health
	Dental surgery
	Hygiene and Tropical Medicine
	Neurology
	Ophthalmology

208. We do not wish to take a dogmatic view of the best shape for these linkages. Space constraints and academic links may lead to other associations than those shown above. Nor do these principal linkages preclude links with other schools. This should be for discussion by the institutions concerned within the overall framework we have described, taking account of the service changes which we propose earlier in this report in relation to the SHAs and the review of specialties.

Postgraduate and continuing training in the NHS

209. The regional postgraduate deans are responsible for coordinating NHS training for junior doctors and others on behalf of the RHAs and the University. We ***recommend*** that the deans should be more closely identified with their regions and the individual medical faculties, rather than being located together within the BPMF. We note that there have been some difficulties in securing rotational training within the SHA hospitals. We

therefore ***recommend*** that the regional postgraduate deans should have equal power in relation to planning training in the present SHAs, as elsewhere.

210. We have referred earlier to the importance of enhancing facilities for postgraduate and continuing education and training for GPs, to enable the development of general practice which we wish to see in London, and an increase in the teaching of undergraduates in primary care settings. We ***recommend*** that additional facilities be developed for such postgraduate training.

Dental schools

211. Dental hospitals exist mainly for teaching, and dental SIFTR is intended to cover 85% of their costs. This means that the effects of the NHS market on patient flow are much less significant than for hospitals teaching medical students. We do not therefore propose any change in the number of dental students in London. The dental schools at King's, the Royal London and UMDS would become part of the multi-faculty institutions which we recommend. The combined dental intake of King's/UMDS would be the largest in the UK but, given this more secure patient base, it should be manageable in terms of clinical teaching facilities. Once both schools are part of a single multi-faculty college, we ***recommend*** that a unified dental school be established. Its ability adequately to teach its enlarged intake should be monitored by the HEFCE.

Nursing and the professions allied to medicine

212. The new arrangements established under Working Paper 10 have had considerable impact on pre- and post-registration training for nurses and the professions allied to medicine (PAMs). Regions now have the lead responsibility for assessing the number of training places required in the light of service needs, and those of the voluntary sector and other bodies, and for placing training contracts. Education providers meet the costs of some provision, and should in any case be consulted where regions' plans affect them.

213. Our findings on the likely volume of acute sector activity in the future, and our recommendations for the development of primary and community health services, will have major implications for this training, which regions will need to take into account. For pre-registration training, regions will need to consider the total volume of training places required, and the size and location of colleges of nursing. Regions will also need to review both the volume and nature of post-registration courses. Fewer specialist courses in hospitals may be needed in the future. For those nurses relocating from the acute sector to community services, training will be needed to prepare them for new ways of working. It is most important that the four Thames regions

and higher education institutions collaborate in all of this. Similar considerations will apply to the training of PAMs.

214. We ***recommend*** that the Implementation Group to which we refer in paragraph 255 should ensure that the Thames RHAs and education providers plan and manage the education and training of nurses and PAMs on a pan-London basis.

215. Research and development in community nursing lags behind that in hospital nursing. This is undesirable for four main reasons. First, we envisage an increase in activity in this sector, compared to the hospital sector. Secondly, there will be fewer young people in the population in the coming years, and this may reduce the availability of candidates for the nursing profession generally. Thirdly, Project 2000 nurses and NVQ trained assistants are now appearing in the community health services, but their skills and training are different to those of their predecessors. Finally, although standards for nursing services are being developed, and there are the beginnings of clinical audit, traditional roles are still carried out with little exploration of their efficiency and effectiveness. We ***recommend*** that greater investment be made in R & D in community nursing to help ensure that high quality and cost-effective care is developed, and that the available mix of nursing skills, including those of practice nurses, is used to maximum advantage.

MANPOWER AND FINANCIAL IMPLICATIONS

REDUCING MANPOWER

216. Reductions in acute sector capacity are bound to require corresponding reductions in manpower. It is apparent that past failures to reduce consultant numbers, in line with past reductions in service capacity in London, are already aggravating the financial difficulties in which several hospitals find themselves in the current year. Reducing manpower will need sensitive but firm management if it is to be accomplished within the short timescale within which supply and demand for acute health care in London must be brought into balance.

217. Much of the problem lies in a ''top-heavy'' medical staffing structure in many London hospitals, beyond that justified by present or future service requirements or academic commitments. If the inner London undergraduate teaching hospitals were to use the same number of consultants per episode of care as the average teaching hospital elsewhere in England, they would need around 450 fewer consultants to deal with current levels of activity. If patient inflows to all the inner London hospitals (including the SHAs) reduced to the maximum extent illustrated in Table 2 on page 22, 680 fewer consultants would be needed. Clearly, however, where patient flows move to other areas, additional demand for consultant manpower will arise in those areas.

218. Our recommendations for reduction in capacity and rationalisation of services will result in fewer consultants being needed in inner London in future, and will require some movement of medical staff within London. The precise extent of the oversupply of consultants, and the specialties which will be affected, will not be clear until the completion of the reviews recommended in paragraph 150. At the same time the implementation of *Achieving a Balance*, and the development of services outside inner London, will require increases in consultant numbers in other parts of England. It will be important that, as far as possible, the skills of consultant medical staff currently working in London are retained within the NHS as a whole.

219. Health authorities have commented to us on the difficulties they have faced in the past in trying to increase medical mobility. We doubt whether the Department of Health has been sufficiently vigorous in putting in place agreed policies for smoothing this process. While we accept that a near-monopsonist employer - especially if it is the state - must be especially sensitive in its manpower and personnel policies, we believe that central action is required to facilitate consultant mobility. If improved arrangements for consultant mobility cannot be negotiated, redundancy and the attendant extended appeal process will be unavoidable, leading to considerable delay and cost in implementing our recommendations.

220. We understand that the Department plans to discuss with the medical profession arrangements for improving consultant mobility, and other measures for handling a potential surplus of consultants in inner London. We would urge that these discussions proceed rapidly and in a constructive fashion. In the meantime, we ***recommend*** that employing authorities should scrutinise closely every consultant post that comes up for appointment, to ensure that filling it is in the long-term interests of the service. It is clearly important that all consultants who are potentially to be made redundant should receive proper assistance and counselling, and where appropriate retraining, to help them to find new posts. A coordinated approach to ensuring that potentially redundant consultants are aware of posts outside inner London should be explored.

221. Reductions in consultant numbers should go hand in hand with reductions in the number of posts held by doctors in training. Given the fact that junior doctors are on fixed term contracts, many for very short periods, these reductions should be rather easier to achieve than those for consultants. In overall terms, London currently has a rather higher proportion of junior doctors to consultants than is found in the rest of the country. A reduction of junior posts in London should, in principle, allow for redistribution of post approvals to other Regions. We are aware of the recent initiative to reduce junior doctors' hours, the ''New Deal'', and would expect the reductions in posts to be managed in such a way that the ''New Deal'' targets are still met in London as well as in the rest of the country.

222. For all other staff groups, including nurses, PAMs, scientists, ancillary staff and managers, there will be inevitable reductions in numbers as hospital capacity in inner London is reduced. For some of these staff, there will be new opportunities opening up elsewhere, as acute services are expanded in outer London and beyond and provision of primary and community services in inner London is increased. We would not wish to underestimate the difficulties that individuals may face during the period of transition, but we would hope that the changing face of London's health services will be seen as providing new and different opportunities. For all those who wish or need to move, including those with specialist skills and knowledge, arrangements should be made to minimise the disruption to individuals and the service. It is important that these arrangements are seen to be fair and consistent across the Thames regions. We therefore ***recommend*** that measures to facilitate the possible redeployment and relocation of staff should be explored.

FINANCIAL SAVINGS

223. Although there will be a reduction in the number of beds in the acute sector in inner London, the purchasers and providers in inner London will not reap all the savings. Where the new system transfers funds to outer districts, which then spend them locally, inner London does not realise a saving. It must instead mitigate a loss by ensuring that the resources which those funds

had supported are redeployed productively. The outer districts do enjoy a revenue saving, owing to the service concerned being delivered at a lower cost (ie outside inner London). The amount of this saving would depend upon the actual extent of the withdrawal of patient flows into inner London, and on actual cost differences. On the basis of average costs, and of the scenarios set out in Table 2 on page 22, we estimate that this saving would be up to £28 million a year at current prices.

224. In principle, the value of capital assets released by this movement of money, and hence patients, out of London, ought to be redistributed, but we ***recommend*** that the net proceeds of asset disposals should be held and managed on a pan-Thames basis to ease the transitional process. We make further proposals on this in paragraph 227.

225. Inner London does gain a saving where providers achieve greater efficiency in delivering their services. In this case the benefit accrues directly to the providers concerned, and, through their correspondingly lower prices, to the purchasers which use them, in terms of increased volume or quality of service. On the basis of the scenarios for increased efficiency set out in Table 2 on page 22, we estimate that this saving would be up to £54 million a year at current prices. We ***recommend*** that these savings should be used to help the process of change in London, and in particular to shift the balance of expenditure between the acute and the community sectors.

NHS TRANSITIONAL COSTS

226. As we have noted throughout this report, there will be transitional costs in building up primary and community services, and in enabling contraction in the acute sector. Examples of such costs are: capital bridging until land sales yield cash; ''double-banking'' of services to avoid gaps; redundancy compensation for surplus manpower. In the medium and long term, change should be at least cost-neutral, as facilities are matched more closely to the level of need, and services are provided more efficiently.

NHS CAPITAL DISPOSALS

227. Many of our recommendations are aimed at achieving a broadly balanced market in which purchasers and providers, the latter increasingly being NHS trusts, can operate with relatively little regulation. However during the transitional period of reorganisation, we believe that rather more regulation will be required. We ***recommend***, during this period, the suspension of the presumption that the proceeds of assets disposals should remain in the hands of the trusts concerned. Such disposals should normally be seen as windfall capital gains, and should be recycled for the benefit of the reorganisation of the NHS in London as a whole. Correspondingly, we

recommend that a new trust should be vested with only those assets which are relevant to its long-term future. Assets which are intended for disposal or alternative use, but which need to be managed by the trust in the meantime, should be transferred to the trust only on a lease for the specific purpose.

UNIVERSITY COSTS

228. There will be capital costs for London University for restructuring, some of which were already planned before our report. But there will be growing calls on HEFCE capital funds as non-medical student numbers nationally increase. We believe that proposals for medical capital developments in London University must be realistic, taking account of the major investment already made by the UFC in London medicine.

229. We ***recommend*** that the aim should be for the costs of rationalisation to be self-financing by sales of medical school assets, redeployment of planned UFC capital funding for London medical schools, and reinvestment of the medical school share of embedded accommodation where NHS assets are sold. We recognise that nonetheless there may be calls for HEFCE funds for bridging capital. The HEFCE will need to consider this within its available resources and overall priorities. This process should involve consultation with the NHS as part of the implementation arrangements we describe below. Although desirable, co-location of medical schools and multi-faculty institutions and rationalisation of pre-clinical and clinical facilities will need to be contingent on the release of funds to finance it.

230. We recognise that asset disposals may not be straightforward, because of planning and other restrictions. But responses from the medical schools suggest that there is a substantial stock of medical school assets, including embedded hospital accommodation, which should make a large contribution to the necessary costs of rationalisation once they are realised. We ***recommend*** that the schools concerned make an early start in planning the rationalisation of their assets, and in preparing the case for reinvestment of the Exchequer proceeds. We ***recommend*** that planning should have regard to the substantial investment made by the MRC and medical research charities in medical schools and teaching hospitals in London, and to the maintenance of the research in which they are involved. To the extent that such research funders own a share of physical assets, they should receive a share of any proceeds from rationalisation.

WEIGHTED CAPITATION

231. We have not attempted a detailed study of the implementation of weighted capitation, either at national, or at sub-regional, levels. However we believe that further work needs to be undertaken to ensure that the approach is systematic and fair. We have no desire to roll back the proper application of the principle of weighted capitation, but we have not seen convincing evidence that it is always applied fairly to inner London districts. Our concerns focus on three issues: health needs, market forces, and transparency.

232. Health needs are extremely difficult to measure, and to allow for in any capitation formula. As a proxy for morbidity, the Department of Health currently uses SMRs up to the age of 75, in its weighted capitation formula for regional allocations. This SMR is a rather better proxy for morbidity than the full age-range SMR. At sub-regional level, use of SMRs could give a distorted picture of health need in inner London, due to the disproportionate tendency for elderly people to move to nursing homes outside London, where their death is then recorded. As a result the inner London district which supported the antecedent morbidity gains no "benefit" from the death statistic. The use of age-limited SMRs will largely avoid this, but Thames RHAs should take this factor into account in devising formulae for district allocations. We understand that the Department is currently preparing for a review of weighted capitation for regional allocations and, as part of this, has consulted widely on the technical problems.

233. London health districts are less homogeneous than most, being a dense patchwork of often stark contrasts in socio-economic and health status. In such circumstances averages can be misleading. Measures of deprivation are, in any case, only a proxy for the real business of the NHS: morbidity. We understand that new census data on long-term limiting illness should become available in mid-1993, and we ***recommend*** that the inclusion of these data in the formula be urgently tested.

234. We are not convinced that the weighting given to some inner London districts adequately reflects the number and higher morbidity of homeless people concentrated there. Two districts have reported that their hospitals make up to 10% of their admissions from street and bed and breakfast homeless people. It is therefore important that the funding of such DHAs as purchasers reflects this burden, and we ***recommend*** that RHAs should review their capitation formulae to ensure that it does so.

235. Likewise we are not convinced that the allowance within capitation formulae for the unavoidable excess costs of services which have to be secured in London (principally the costs of pay, land and buildings) are appropriate. For land and buildings we understand that the Department of Health has recently concluded work on a method of distributing capital

charges funding to regions, once this regime moves away from "neutrality"; and that this compensates for regional differences in these costs. However the Thames regions must adequately reflect the exceptionally high costs in London in their own formulae. We note also that although weighted capitation formulae can reflect actual differentials in labour costs, the rigidities of the NHS pay system can make it difficult for the money to have the intended effect. We ***recommend*** that these issues be kept under review to ensure that market forces factors are truly reflected in capitation formulae.

236. At a sub-regional level, we have observed wide variations in the apparent levels of capitation between neighbouring districts which we doubt are due simply to differences in need. We are aware, of course, that differences in regional top-slicing policies, the provision of regional specialties, etc, make a simple comparison of district allocations per capita misleading. Furthermore, each region seems to be moving towards the goal of weighted capitation at different speeds. However we believe that this lack of transparency is itself undesirable.

237. In paragraph 253 we recommend that there should be a mechanism for ensuring pan-London consistency in several key areas of NHS policy: we ***recommend*** that a uniform approach to the calculation of and progress towards weighted capitation at the district level should be included in this.

OTHER ISSUES

238. There are a number of issues which we have not pursued in any depth, but which are worth mentioning briefly.

AMBULANCE SERVICES

239. The effective provision of ambulance services is central to good quality accident and emergency treatment and the efficient utilisation of hospital resources. We note that the London Ambulance Service (LAS) has many problems peculiar to the capital, including the size of population covered and adverse traffic conditions. Although many specific problems with ambulance services have been reported to us during the course of our work, we believe these are best addressed through local management action by the LAS and the health authorities. Accordingly we do not intend to make any specific recommendations about the LAS.

THE PUBLIC HEALTH FUNCTION

240. We have had discussions with those involved in public health who expressed to us their concerns about the management of communicable disease in London. They pointed out that the focus of the reformed NHS on either the commissioning, or the provision, of health services left no explicit responsibility for such matters. They feared that lack of communication between regions, hospitals (in particular NHS trusts), and environmental health officers, could lead to circumstances in which a major epidemic might develop with no-one specifically responsible for ensuring adequate communication and control. We ***recommend*** that London should be treated as a whole, as far as public health is concerned, with a formal mechanism for taking decisive action, and for assuming control of key facilities, in appropriate circumstances.

DENTAL SERVICES

241. In the time available we have not been able to make a special study of NHS dental services in the capital. However we are aware that for some time some London dentists have been reluctant to take on new NHS patients. This is especially noticeable in many of the ''deprived'' inner city areas. We believe that FHSAs should explore alternative mechanisms for providing NHS dental care in such areas.

Private healthcare

242. We have not considered the role of the private healthcare sector in London for two reasons. First, although there are many private hospitals in London with a significant patient throughput serving patients from a wide area, there is little information readily available about their activity. Secondly, although it is likely that private sector provision, and in particular the uptake of health insurance, has an impact on local demand for NHS services, we do not believe that this should influence our strategic review of acute sector capacity.

IMPLEMENTATION

243. The changes we recommend in this report cannot be put in place overnight. Within the NHS, the continuity and quality of patient service is paramount. In the academic sphere, excellence must be preserved while the system undergoes cultural and organisational change. As far as possible the impetus for change should develop organically from the institutions in London themselves. However there is a major, and continuing, management task ahead. It is essential that priorities are set, and a mechanism for implementing them is put in place.

PRIORITIES FOR CHANGE IN THE NHS

244. We have recommended major change to a number of inner London hospitals. It is of paramount importance that decisions about these hospitals are taken as quickly as possible, subject to the necessary consultation procedures. In a number of cases, we have proposed specific further work to determine the way forward. It is essential that this work is set in hand forthwith and conclusions rapidly reached. Decisions about the hospitals as service institutions fall to the NHS. Close consultation with the HEFCE and the University will be required to ensure that the interests of education and research are safeguarded. We ***recommend*** that decisions on hospitals requiring major change be taken as soon as possible.

245. The development of primary and community health services forms an essential part of our recommendations and must go hand in hand with the rationalisation and reduction of capacity in the hospital sector. It is clear that savings to be made from the changes to the acute sector will take time to be realised. We therefore ***recommend*** that resources for the development of the primary and community health services, to pump-prime and provide transitional support, be urgently secured.

246. We place great importance on the inclusion of the SHAs' capacity in the rationalisation of inner London's acute sector capacity. We therefore ***recommend*** that steps be taken immediately to ensure that the SHAs are brought into the internal market within an appropriate funding framework.

247. Within the framework of the reduced hospital estate, a thorough review should be made of the distribution of services across London, including the capacity of the SHAs, in order to rationalise the provision of specialties. We have already recommended that working parties be formed to take forward these reviews and outlined their composition. We ***recommend*** that the Implementation Group recommended below places priority on the setting up of these working parties so that they may start work as soon as possible.

248. We attach great importance to the establishment of joint planning between the University and the NHS in implementing the changes we recommend in this report. In order for the full benefits of our proposals to be realised, we ***recommend*** that there should be close cooperation between the NHS, the University and the HEFCE over the timetable and financial arrangements for hospital mergers and closures, and other service changes. In this way, the medical faculties will have sufficient time to reorganise and plan a revised curriculum around service needs. There will also need to be discussion between the University and the HEFCE about the timetable for transferring student places out of London without undue disruption.

249. In terms of timescale, the key priority is to secure the mergers of the undergraduate schools into the framework we have described. A number of these mergers are already well-advanced, notably those between UMDS and King's College (which includes King's College medical school); and the Charing Cross and Westminster medical school with Imperial College (which includes St Mary's medical school). We ***recommend*** that these be pursued and implemented with all speed.

250. We ***recommend*** that mergers take place as soon as possible between the Royal Free Hospital medical school and University College, and between Bart's and the Royal London medical schools and Queen Mary and Westfield College.

251. It is for the University and the schools concerned to take this forward in the first instance. However, we believe that the risk to the future of teaching and research in London if these proposals are not implemented is so great that we ***recommend*** that action should be taken by the HEFCE to secure them if necessary.

252. We have said that integration of the postgraduate schools into the faculties of medicine must take place at a slower pace. This pace will be influenced by changes in the organisation of London University and in funding for the SHAs, both of which are likely to lead to pressure for greater integration. Nonetheless, we believe that progress in establishing links between the medical postgraduate institutions and the multi-faculty colleges should be subject to external scrutiny. We therefore ***recommend*** that the HEFCE should monitor the development of such links and mount a review of their effectiveness in consultation with London University in five years' time, when the reorganisation of the undergraduate medical schools should be nearing completion.

A MECHANISM FOR IMPLEMENTING CHANGE

253. Many of the problems we address in this report have arisen from the lack of a mechanism for ensuring that decisions which are sensible at a regional level also make sense at the pan-London level. We do not consider that the proper way to achieve this is through a further statutory tier, nor do we believe that a specific London Health Authority would be desirable. We ***recommend*** that a mechanism needs to be created for coordinating, across the four Thames regions and the University, consistent approaches to such matters as capital investment, formulae for and rate of progress towards capitation funding, medical and non-medical manpower planning, education and training, the provision of high-cost specialties, public health and many other matters.

254. In addition, we have set out a major agenda for reform which cannot be effectively discharged by the individual health authorities on their own. If the changes which we believe are necessary are to be achieved within the timescale which we are convinced is essential, they will need to be driven briskly by a dedicated Implementation Group. We welcome the announcement earlier this year that the Government intends to establish such a body.

255. We ***recommend*** that this Implementation Group should be answerable to the Secretaries of State, and should be closely linked to the NHS Management Executive and to the HEFCE. A small group rather like our present team should be set up under an experienced chairman. Unlike our own group, however, this Implementation Group should have clear executive responsibilities, and the power to allocate and withhold funds. We hasten to say that none of us wishes to put ourselves forward for this task.

256. The implementation of many of our recommendations will take time to plan and execute. This inevitable time-lag will tend to sap morale. In order to minimise this, and to avoid damaging ''planning blight'', it will be important that Ministers do at least set out quickly and unequivocally their key decisions about the direction of change in London. We ***recommend*** that you should announce at the earliest opportunity the constitution of the Implementation Group, so that they can start to acquaint themselves with their task. Clearly they cannot implement decisions which Ministers have still to take, but they could start straight away on organising the specialty reviews, so that the results can be acted upon as soon as possible, and can inform Ministers' subsequent decisions. We ***recommend*** that decisions on the key changes proposed in this report should follow as soon as possible thereafter.

15 October 1992

BERNARD TOMLINSON
MICHAEL BOND
PEARL BROWN
MOLLIE MCBRIDE

Printed in the United Kingdom for HMSO.
Dd. 0295524, C95, 10/92, 3396/4, 5673, 218326.

TEACHING HOSPITALS & MAIN DGHS
CAM
South West Hertfordshire
Enfield
Barnet
Harrow
Haringey
Waltham Forest
Redbridge
Hampstead
City and Hackney
Parkside
Hillingdon
Ealing
Bloomsbury & Islington
Tower Hamlets
Newham
Riverside
Greenwich
Richmond, Twickenham and Roehampton
West Lambeth
Camberwell
Bexley
Wandsworth
Lewisham and North Southwark
Hounslow and Spelthorne
Merton and Sutton
Kingston and Esher
Bromley
Croydon
North West Surrey
TEACHING HOSPITALS
A St BARTHOLOMEWS
B CHARING CROSS
C St GEORGE'S
D GUY'S
E KINGS COLLEGE
F St MARY'S
G ROYAL FREE
H ROYAL LONDON
I St THOMAS'S
J UNIVERSITY COLLEGE
K WESTMINSTER AND CHELSEA
OTHER INNER LONDON HOSPITALS
L CENTRAL MIDDLESEX
M HAMMERSMITH
N HOMERTON
O LEWISHAM
P NEWHAM GENERAL
Q WHITTINGTON
OUTER LONDON HOSPITALS
R BARNET GREEN
S BROMLEY
T BROOK GENERAL
U EALING
V EDGWARE GENERAL
W GREENWICH DISTRICT GENERAL
X St HELIER'S
Y KINGSTON
Z MAYDAY
AA NORTH MIDDLESEX
AB NORTHWICK PARK
AC QUEEN MARY'S ROEHAMPTON
AD WEST MIDDLESEX
AE WHIPPS CROSS
ED's (census enumeration districts)
DHA boundary
10 minute drive time
NOTE Drive times are calculated assuming
Monday–Friday,daytime,offpeak
Road speeds
Scale is 1:149450
ED's courtesy of NOMIS
DHA boundaries courtesy of NOMIS
© CAM Ltd-071 232 1111 200 ALASKA WORKS,61 GRANGE RD,LONDON SE1 3BH

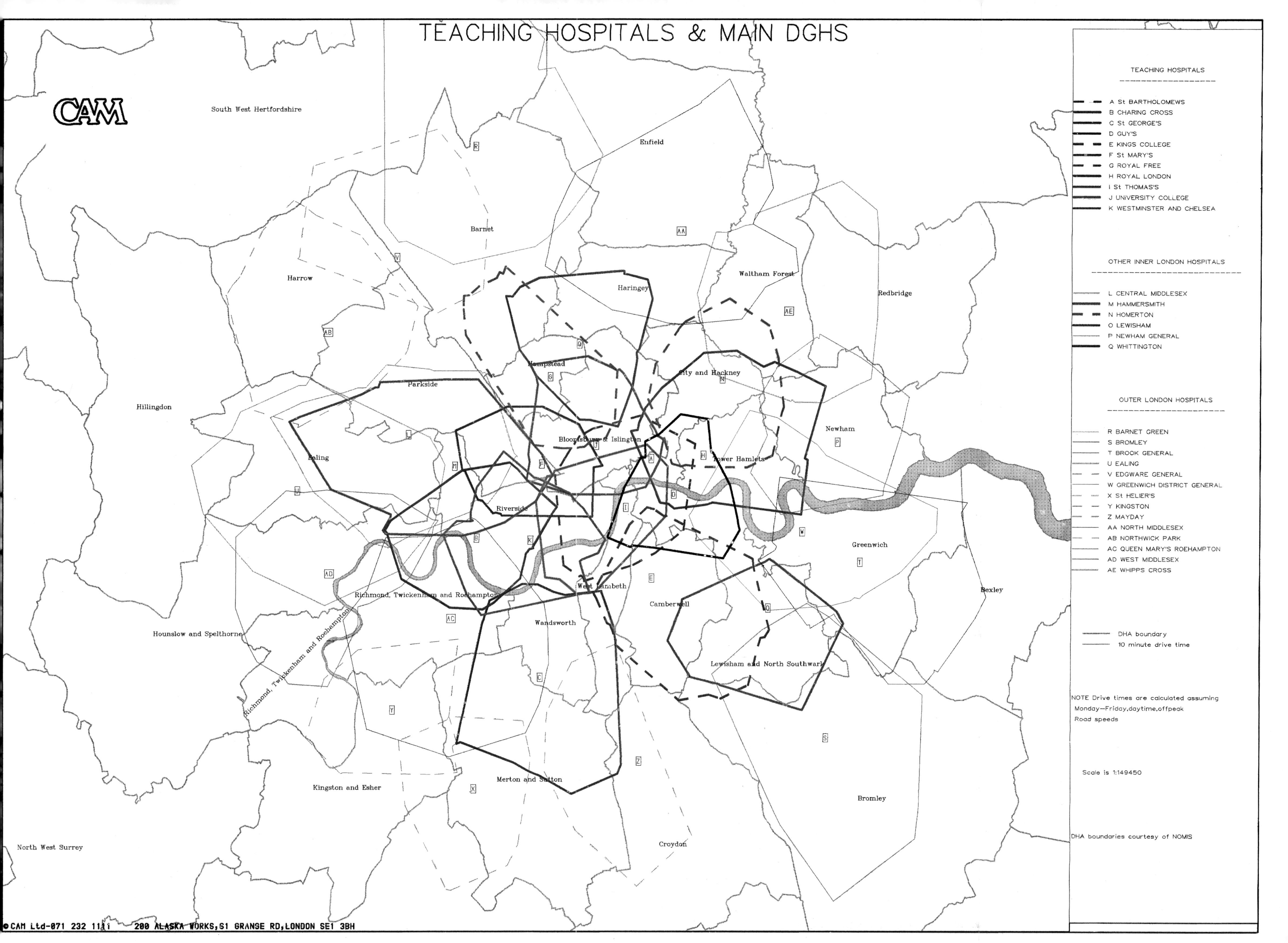
TEACHING HOSPITALS & MAIN DGHS
CAM
South West Hertfordshire
Enfield
Barnet
Harrow
Haringey
Waltham Forest
Redbridge
Hillingdon
Hampstead
City and Hackney
Parkside
Bloomsbury & Islington
Newham
Ealing
Tower Hamlets
Riverside
Greenwich
Bexley
West Lambeth
Richmond, Twickenham and Roehampton
Camberwell
Wandsworth
Hounslow and Spelthorne
Lewisham and North Southwark
Merton and Sutton
Kingston and Esher
Bromley
North West Surrey
Croydon
TEACHING HOSPITALS
A St BARTHOLOMEWS
B CHARING CROSS
C St GEORGE'S
D GUY'S
E KINGS COLLEGE
F St MARY'S
G ROYAL FREE
H ROYAL LONDON
I St THOMAS'S
J UNIVERSITY COLLEGE
K WESTMINSTER AND CHELSEA
OTHER INNER LONDON HOSPITALS
L CENTRAL MIDDLESEX
M HAMMERSMITH
N HOMERTON
O LEWISHAM
P NEWHAM GENERAL
Q WHITTINGTON
OUTER LONDON HOSPITALS
R BARNET GREEN
S BROMLEY
T BROOK GENERAL
U EALING
V EDGWARE GENERAL
W GREENWICH DISTRICT GENERAL
X St HELIER'S
Y KINGSTON
Z MAYDAY
AA NORTH MIDDLESEX
AB NORTHWICK PARK
AC QUEEN MARY'S ROEHAMPTON
AD WEST MIDDLESEX
AE WHIPPS CROSS
DHA boundary
10 minute drive time
NOTE Drive times are calculated assuming Monday—Friday,daytime,offpeak Road speeds
Scale is 1:149450
DHA boundaries courtesy of NOMIS
©CAM Ltd-071 232 1111 200 ALASKA WORKS,61 GRANGE RD,LONDON SE1 3BH